How could Gala continue seeing Conrad Brandon when she knew what type of man he was—and what he had once done to her family?

ICE PRINCESS

BY

MADELEINE KER

MILLS & BOON LIMITED
15–16 BROOK'S MEWS
LONDON W1A 1DR

*First published in Great Britain 1985
by Mills & Boon Limited*

© Madeleine Ker 1985

*Australian copyright 1985
Philippine copyright 1985
This edition 1985*

ISBN 0 263 75007 8

Set in Monophoto Plantin 10 on 11 pt.
01–0485 – 54270

*Made and printed in Great Britain by
Richard Clay (The Chaucer Press) Ltd,
Bungay, Suffolk*

CHAPTER ONE

IT hadn't been a very good morning. Her eldest brother Michael had been home on one of his rare spells of leave last night. He'd also been celebrating his promotion to senior pilot, and after a happy dinner at their parents' house in East Sussex, he'd taken her out for what had turned out to be a very late evening in London with Jack, her other brother, and various members of the flying fraternity. During the course of the evening, she'd drunk rather more champagne than she was used to. She'd woken up with a slight hangover and a feeling of distinct regret for last night's excesses, and she wasn't in the mood for broken appointments.

Gala Fletcher flipped impatiently through her appointment book. Yes, it was there, all right—*Mr Brandon, 11:00 a.m. Preliminary examination.* By the precise Swiss watch pinned to the front of her starched white smock, it was now 11:15. She pulled a face. Unpunctual patients were the bane of her life.

She picked up the telephone, and rang Nita Westbroke at Reception.

'Parker Clinic, Reception,' cooed the slightly bored voice.

'Nita? It's Gala Fletcher. I wonder if you know where a Mr . . .' She consulted the page again. 'A Mr Brandon might be? He's late for physiotherapy.'

Nita's voice took on a flicker of interest. 'Would that be Conrad Brandon? Mean, moody and magnificent?'

'I've no idea,' Gala said shortly. 'I've just got his name down in my appointment book.'

5

'You lucky thing. I wish he was down in *my* appointment book!'

'Furthermore,' Gala added, sorting through her files, 'I don't seem to have any notes on him from the doctors.'

'He only booked in yesterday,' Nita said. Gala could hear her flipping through her own notes. 'He's here for general R and R. Referred by Sir Lionel.'

'Rest and Recuperation.' Gala pulled a face. That was sometimes a polite euphemism for drying out after an alcoholic binge. 'Well, do you know where he is right now?'

'Hang on.' There was a pause, then Nita's voice came back. 'My informants tell me he'll most likely be at the pool. That's apparently where he's spent most of his time since he arrived.'

'Well he's kept me waiting for fifteen minutes,' Gala said drily. 'In fact, almost twenty, now. Could you get someone to call him, Nita? This will throw the whole day's schedule out for me if I don't get it sorted.'

'Hold on.'

Gala sighed, tucking the 'phone into the crook of her neck, and got on with some case-notes. It never ceased to amaze her that people who paid as much for their medical treatment as patients at the Parker Clinic did could be so casual about breaking appointments. People came here for a variety of reasons—to recover from nervous breakdowns, to dry out, to lose weight, even as a kind of status-laden holiday—but a lot of them had one thing in common. Money.

If you weren't lucky enough to be referred here on the National Health, you had to be prepared to pay several hundred pounds a week for your treatment. The best didn't come cheap, and the Parker was the best of its kind in southern England.

That was one of the things that kept her here, despite the revulsion she felt for the pampered, drink-sodden *nouveau riches* who occasionally found their way into this famous hospital and treated it like a hotel. It was a superb healing centre, equipped with the best machinery and staff, and run by professionals. But you still got people like Mr Brandon, who spent hundreds of pounds to come here and lounge by the pool all day long.

Conrad Brandon. Wait a minute.

Conrad Brandon. Her pen froze over the paper. There was something dreadfully familiar about that name. She didn't have to search far into her memories to find out why. When Crystal Warren had walked out on her brother, a week before their wedding-day, it had been for a man named Conrad Brandon. A man named Conrad Brandon who'd taken her to Barbados, leaving Jack stunned and disbelieving. That had been three years ago, and she knew that the pain of that betrayal was still with Jack. Of course it would be. Her brother had adored the slim, blonde Crystal with every fibre of his generous heart; and though Gala had to admit that she'd never wholly liked Crystal, none of them had dreamed that she could behave like that.

'Gala . . .'

She shrugged the phone back to her mouth, her eyes still unseeing. 'Yes?'

'I'm sorry, love—everyone seems to be frightfully busy at the moment. Could you nip down to the pool yourself and see if he's there? It's only down two corridors from your office.'

'Okay—Nita, are you sure his name is *Conrad* Brandon?' Gala asked.

'Sure,' came the reply. Gala gnawed her lip, trying to remember. The man who'd taken Crystal away from Jack had been some kind of celebrity, a film-star or something—Nita's voice cut into her thoughts. 'He's the champion rally driver, you must have heard of him.'

'Yes.' It was starting to click now. 'Yes,' Gala said quietly, 'I believe I have heard of him.'

'Well, I'm afraid the office is deserted, love. Will you be able to find him yourself?'

'If I must. Thanks, Nita.' She put down the receiver, and stared into space with wide green eyes. It *had* to be the same man. She could even hear his name on Crystal's lips, remember the matter-of-fact way she'd announced that her marriage to Jack, planned and dreamed about for six months, wasn't going to take place. She'd told them all, in the living-room of her parents' house. Gala had been still living there then, in her last year at college. *Con's taking me to Jamaica. I guess I'm just not ready to settle down yet. I'm sorry if I've hurt anyone.* Hurt anyone? Gala winced as she remembered her parents' dazed faces, the pain and the shame in Jack's eyes.

Could she possibly treat this man—if it *was* the same man? For a second she thought of ringing Roger Trefusis, the other physiotherapist at the Clinic, and asking him to take this patient on. But then she rejected the idea. She wanted to see Conrad Brandon, take a look at the kind of man who had caused her family so much misery.

She got up slowly and walked out into the corridor. Tall for a woman, and blessed with a slender, supple body, Gala Fletcher moved with innate grace, and the severe lines of her smock couldn't disguise the elegant lines of the figure beneath. Her mouth, normally full and somehow vulnerable, was now compressed into a taut line.

As if to emphasise her mood, she gathered the rich auburn hair that curled softly around her face, and pulled it back into a simple pony-tail. Doing so revealed the soft curves of a face that was emerging from the prettiness of youth into the full beauty of womanhood. Gala was twenty-four, and though her jade-green eyes and generous mouth didn't always hold the authority she'd have liked to possess, there was something in her face that automatically commanded male attention. Perhaps it was the way those eyes slanted mysteriously at the corners, or perhaps it was the air of almost fragile defiance about the way they looked out at the world; but their expression was arresting. Even intriguing.

Perhaps men were interested for the very reason that they sensed she wasn't really interested in them.

She'd intended to walk to the sliding doors of the glassed-in, heated pool, and simply call his name out. But when she got there, the pool was unexpectedly crowded. Bright February sunlight had drawn the patients like bees to a honeypot, and the water was full of pink bodies, mostly overweight and middle-aged. The pale winter sky made a strange canopy for the tropical warmth of the area. Someone was tossing a beachball in the water. The prospect of bawling for the elusive Mr Brandon like a children's governess didn't appeal to her at all. She walked over to where Freddie Griffiths, the muscular blond lifeguard, had his perch.

'What brings you here, Gala?' He smiled, blue eyes dropping frankly to appraise her figure Freddie's beefy good looks exerted a strong appeal for a certain kind of woman. Several of the orderlies were crazy about him, and Freddie was reputed to extend his activities after-hours with some of the older and wealthier female patients. Gala herself hated that kind of rumour. She preferred to think that all the staff were professional people with professional ethics, but found herself speculating about the chunky gold bracelet that glittered on Freddie's thick wrist.

'I'm looking for a patient who should be at physiotherapy now,' she told him, looking away from

the bauble. 'His name is Brandon. You wouldn't know
whether he's here, would you?'

'Conrad Brandon?' Freddie grinned. 'The rally
driver? No wonder you're chasing after him!'

'I'm not chasing after him,' Gala retorted coldly. 'Is
he here?'

'Sure,' Freddie nodded, still grinning. He pointed
to the far end of the pool, which was less popular with
the patients, because it was deeper. 'That's the golden
boy. Lying on the red towel.'

'Thanks.' She felt Freddie's china-blue eyes on her
back as she walked quickly round the pool. A strange,
chilled feeling was turning her anger into something
unpleasantly like nervousness.

She stopped a few feet from him, then moved slowly
and silently forward. Utterly unlike the vast majority
of the patients here, he was neither overweight nor
middle-aged. The body that lay, apparently asleep, on
the wine-red towel was muscular and tanned to a deep
mahogany. The black Speedo hugged athletically slim
hips and a hard bottom like a matador's. Anyone less
obviously in need of the Clinic's attention would be
hard to imagine. That thought changed her strange
fear back into anger again. She couldn't stop people
treating this Clinic like a holiday home, but this man
was due for physiotherapy. And physiotherapy he was
going to get, no matter who or what he was.

He was lying on his stomach, his head turned to one
side. Gala stopped next to him, and stared down at the
lean face at her feet. Only a man. The planes of the
face were unforgiving, aggressively masculine. A dark
shadow of beard gave him a sardonic, saturnine look.
The eyelashes were long and black, but there was
nothing soft about the face. And nothing particularly
happy, either. Even in sleep, the man seemed to be
clenching his jaws angrily.

'Mr Brandon,' she said sharply, interrupting her

own survey. She saw tension knot the powerful muscles of his back. Then he rolled over. His eyes opened to lazy, cloudy blue slits, and he surveyed her in silence. Suddenly, instinctively, she knew. This was the man who'd stolen Crystal. 'I'm the physio-therapist,' she informed him coldly. 'You're half-an-hour late for your appointment with me.'

'Indeed.' He sat up, running lean fingers through his black hair.

'Indeed,' she echoed angrily. 'They tell me you're a rally driver. I'd have expected someone like you to be rather more adult about time.'

'Really?' He rose to his feet in an unexpectedly smooth movement, and glanced at the solid gold watch on his wrist. 'I fell asleep. When you get to my age, you'll learn that sleep is a precious commodity. You learn to snatch it when it comes.'

'I'll ask Sir Lionel to prescribe some sleeping-pills for you,' she suggested acidly. He couldn't be much more than ten years older than her, and she didn't like being spoken to as though she were a child. A startlingly primitive smudge of dark hair extended from his chest down over his flat stomach and abdomen. He studied her in silence for a moment.

'I suppose you have a name?' he asked.

'Gala Fletcher,' she said shortly, wondering whether there would be any flicker of recognition. There wasn't. The cloudy blue eyes were beautiful, but there was an arrogant, hard expression in them that set her hackles up like a cat facing an intruder. What quality would he have to be able to charm a woman from the very steps of the altar?

'Miss?'

'*Ms*,' she corrected as brusquely as she knew how.

'Miz,' he repeated. An ironic glitter appeared momentarily beneath the thick lashes as he lowered his lids. 'What do you want of me, *Miz* Fletcher?'

'Just your presence in my office,' she answered. 'Can you come along, please? I don't have too much time to waste.' She'd spoken as offensively as she dared, but he didn't seem either offended or amused. He simply stooped and scooped up the beach-robe that had been lying beside him. It was wine-red, to match the luxuriously fluffy towel. The watch, she noted, was a Rolex Oyster. Gala wasn't quite sure what rally driving was, but this Mr Brandon was obviously not unacquainted with the winner's champagne and laurels. Wealth and success sat on his tall, powerful body like some kind of tangible aura. And that was another thing that set her hackles up. In her two years here she'd seen the very worst side of the rich—their self-indulgence, their indifference, their arrogance. This man was obviously wealthy. He carried the authority and self-confidence of someone who was accustomed to being obeyed. It was very easy to see why Crystal Warren had walked out on Jack for this man. Jack was almost handsome, in a lean sort of way, but he simply didn't have this icy devil's style.

'Are you sure you work here?' he enquired in his deep, slightly rough voice.

'Of course I do,' she snapped. 'Why shouldn't I?'

'You don't strike the right note of servile deference,' he observed drily. 'Most of the staff here are only too eager to be trodden on.'

'And you oblige, no doubt?'

'If someone's determined to impersonate an Axminster,' he retorted, 'they can only expect to be walked all over.'

She had to bite back her highly unprofessional anger. For this morning, at least, she was going to have to keep what she knew about him separate from her work. But physiotherapy could be uncomfortable sometimes, and she was suddenly hoping that Conrad Brandon was going to require the most gruelling treatment available. There was something very disturbing about the man, something she didn't like. And he badly needed a jolt of some kind to curb that sardonic tongue. She turned her back on him, and stalked towards the exit without looking to see if he was following.

Halfway down the corridor he caught her up, his fingers biting into her arm painfully.

'Slow down,' he said gently. 'I'm not as fast as you are, Ms Fletcher.' His touch made her flinch like electricity, and she tried to twist her arm away, but he was far too strong. Forced to look at him, she noticed for the first time that he was limping, and reduced her pace. He let go of her arm, and she angrily rubbed the mark of his fingers.

'You don't need to show off your strength, Mr Brandon,' she told him icily. She wasn't used to looking up at men, but Conrad Brandon was a good eight inches taller than her own five-seven. And his stature made her seem frail. She snapped her eyes away from his, and led the way down the next corridor to her office in a crackling silence. The fact that he had some kind of injury after all did not soften her towards him in the slightest.

'It's now almost a quarter to twelve,' she continued in the same unfriendly tone as she shut the door behind them. 'My next patient is at twelve exactly.' She paused to let that sink in. He was watching her with those narrowed, smoky eyes. She went on, 'And I don't have any notes on you. If I can get some idea of what treatment you need, however, this appointment will not have been *entirely* wasted.' She sat down, and picked up her pen. 'Just before I examine you, what exactly are you here for, Mr Brandon? Apart, I mean, from the attractions of sleeping at our poolside.'

'I thought you were going to tell me that.' Unmoved by her sarcasm, he folded his arms. 'I had a

consultation with your esteemed founder in Harley
Street, and he recommended me for a week in
this . . .' He paused. 'This paradise for middle-aged
slimmers.'

'It's rather more than that,' she said sharply. Sir
Lionel Parker, after whom the Clinic had been named,
still practised in Harley Street. If he had recommended
this man for a stay at the Clinic, then it would be
because he needed treatment. It would be up to her to
make her diagnosis as a physiotherapist. She assessed
his wide shoulders, the muscular neck. The male body
was susceptible to physiological injuries, she knew. All
those muscle groups and tendons, all the crazy strains
that men put on their bodies in the name of work or
sport. Or vanity. The majority of her patients were
male, and most of them had hurt themselves through
believing that they were a lot fitter than they really
were. 'As a matter of interest,' she asked, 'what did
you go and see Sir Lionel Parker about? That limp?'

He watched her for a second, then shrugged. 'It
wasn't my idea in the first place. My team manager
more or less kidnapped me to go there. But, yes, my
leg was part of it.'

'What else is there?' she probed.

'I get headaches. Various other pains. Stiffness here
and there. Insomnia. Tiredness.' Gala didn't try and
hide her grimace. Those sounded suspiciously like the
signs of heavy drinking. An occupational hazard, no
doubt, of rich glamour-boys like Mr Brandon. What
sort of life did he lead? Looking closer, there were
tired smudges under those grey-blue eyes, and lines
around his mouth that might have been either pain or
ill-temper. Inconsequentially, she wondered what had
happened to Crystal Warren. Had her fling with this
man been worth losing Jack?

'I see.' She stood up, smoothing her smock over her
hips with a businesslike air. 'I have to make an

examination, Mr Brandon. Would you take off your gown and lie on the couch, please.'

Without speaking, he rose, slipped off the towelling robe, and lay down on the medical couch.

'On your stomach, please,' she commanded. Not relishing her job suddenly, she placed the palms of her hands on his shoulders, probing with expert fingers for the deltoids, the heart-shaped muscles at the tops of the arms, and then traced the trapezius on either side, the cables of muscle that ran from the tops of the arms to the sides of the neck. They were unexpectedly taut, as though their power were straining to erupt into violence. 'Relax, please,' she said quietly.

'I am relaxed,' he grated. She didn't bother to contradict him. He was strong, she could feel that. Strong and tense. She was already absorbed with the vertebrae at the back of his neck. She could tell at once that one or more of them was out of place. The thick muscle that ran down into his back was clenched in spasm. Her mouth tightened. This would be hurting like hell now, and had probably been hurting for weeks. 'How long have you had pains in your neck?' she demanded.

'I can't remember,' he replied calmly. She clicked her tongue irritably.

'You should have been treated weeks ago.' His skin was still warm from the sun, but her attention was now one hundred per cent professional. The magnificent male body that lay under her hands was work. A problem to be solved, nothing else. Tracing the line of his spine between the *latissimus dorsi* muscles, her fingers encountered a pattern familiar from her work with divers and parachutists. 'You get headaches, do you?' she said ironically. 'Do you realise that half your discs are compressed? What do you do, jump out of third-storey windows on to concrete?' There was no answer. She studied the broad back with a mixture of anger and despair. This was a formidably powerful body, but one which was used mercilessly hard. There were several silvery scars to bear witness to past injuries, and the mark of what had probably been an operation to treat a dislocated shoulder.

She pressed her fingers delicately into the small of his back, the lumbar fascia. His almost imperceptible flinch was a tell-tale sign. The whole area was probably aflame with pain.

The sheet of muscle at the side of his left knee was swollen, probably badly torn. Also, the last traces of fading bruises were visible on his thigh. He'd probably blame his limp on that—but she knew there was more to it than an injured knee.

'Roll over, please.' He did so, and stared up at her, an enigmatic smile haunting the corners of his dark-fringed eyes now.

'Well?' he asked quietly, cradling his head in his clasped hands.

'You treat your body like a stock-car,' she said sharply. Under the thick hair on his stomach was the jagged line of another scar, almost six inches long. God knew how he had got these scars over the years. Gala shook her head. 'The only other patient I've ever known who has anything *like* the number of lesions you've got is a movie stuntman.'

But Conrad Brandon was beautifully built, she had to admit that. The breadth of his chest tapered to a slim waist, and his skin was velvety-smooth under her touch. The black triangle of his costume mocked her. There was a naked sensuality about him, about the way he was watching her. Like Freddie at the pool, this man would exert a powerful fascination over women. But where Freddie was placid and leonine, this man was a sleek, dangerous, frightening panther. Again, she felt suddenly disturbed by him, and turned away. 'That's all, Mr

Brandon.' Her mouth was dry. 'Just tell me one thing. Is it worth it?'

'Is what worth it?'

'The way you treat your body,' she replied.

'I'm the British champion.' As though he'd answered her question, he sat up, the muscles of his tanned body coming into relief for a second. 'Can I dress now?' he asked with polite irony.

'Yes.' She stalked back to her desk, and began scribbling notes in silence. She wasn't impressed by the fact that he was a champion at anything. He'd abused his body so badly that it was hard to know where to start. He'd need traction for that neck, and a lot of controlled exercise for his spine for a start. She'd have to tell the room staff to put a fracture board underneath his mattress—he'd need the support. Only one pillow, of course. And she'd have to book him in with Walt or Mona for massage. There was probably more, too. His exhaustion was most likely mental as well as physical. She'd felt that in the tautness of his body, seen it in the lines etched at the corners of his eyes and bracketed round the harsh curve of his mouth. When Sir Lionel had sent him here for 'general rest and recuperation', she guessed, he'd had the man's obvious inner tension as much in mind as his physical injuries. The will to win was something she'd seen in many men. In her brothers Michael and Jack, for example. In Brian Matthews, her first and only lover. And in this man, Conrad Brandon, it burned like a dark flame.

'You look as though you've been sucking a lemon,' he said drily, looking down at her as he belted his robe. 'Am I in that bad shape?'

'How do you feel?' she countered coldly. 'You must be one massive ache, Mr Brandon. I want to see you twice a day for the next week, mid-morning and mid-afternoon. Nita at Reception will give you the appointments tonight at dinner.' She didn't lift her eyes from the file she was writing in. 'Goodbye, Mr Brandon.'

'Miz Fletcher.' She looked up to meet the faintest trace of a mocking smile on his lips.

'Yes?'

'You don't drive an Audi, do you?'

'No,' she said in surprise. 'I don't. Why?'

'They're among my biggest rivals,' he said calmly. 'And something tells me you definitely count me among the opposition. Am I right?'

Leaving her staring at him, he turned on his heel, and walked out. Gala cursed briefly and fiercely under her breath. Her next patient was due in a few minutes, and she was developing a throbbing headache. She pulled open the drawer of her desk, and took out the bottle of aspirin.

Her conviction that this was the same man who'd taken Crystal was stronger than ever. She glanced at her watch. Michael might still be in London—his flight wasn't due until three. Impulsively, she picked up the telephone and dialled the hotel where his airline had booked him in. He was still there, though obviously poised to leave for the airport.

'Mike? It's Gala.'

'Hi, kid! Make it quick, I'm already running twenty minutes late.'

'Just one question,' she promised. 'Remember when Crystal walked out on Jack?'

'Sure.'

'What was his name—the other man?'

'Conrad Brandon.' Michael Fletcher's voice tightened with remembered anger. 'The bastard.'

'Was he a rally driver?' she pressed.

'Yeah, a real hot-shot. He won the British Championship this year, didn't you hear? Damn this tie . . .'

'What happened to Crystal?' Gala asked. 'Did he marry her?'

There was a bark of laughter down the line. 'Marry, hah! His kind don't marry. Only sentimental dopes like Jack marry. I heard he was going with some other woman less than a month after Jack and Crystal split up.'

'No!' she gasped.

'Jet set morals.' She could almost see Mike's broad shoulders shrug. 'I only fly them from place to place. What are all these questions about, anyway?' Gala hesitated. But before she could make up her mind whether or not it would be best to tell Mike that Conrad Brandon was now at the Parker Clinic, he went on, 'Look, I must rush, Gala. If you want to know all the gory details, you'd better ask Jack. I'll see you in ten days, okay?'

'Okay. Don't hit any angels up there.'

'I won't. I had a great time last night, by the way. G'bye, kid.'

She put down the receiver thoughtfully. So it *was* the same man. Her instinct had been right. And now what?

And now *nothing*, she told herself sharply. Conrad Brandon is a patient here. In a few days he'll be gone, and out of your life forever. There's no need for you to rake up the embers of a fire that burned out three long years ago . . .

A discreet knock interrupted her self-lecture, and a patient's head appeared round the door.

'Am I interrupting? Only I've been out here for five minutes . . .'

'Sorry,' Gala smiled, pushing the whole mess to the back of her mind and standing up. 'Come in, Mrs Neill . . .'

At lunchtime, Gala sat at her usual table in the dining-room with Roger Trefusis, the senior physio-

therapist at the Clinic. The staff ate at the same
time as the patients, but in a marked-off section of the
dining-room. Its one glass wall overlooked the expanse
of wooded parkland that the Clinic was set in, letting
in and trapping all the sunshine that was on offer.
Much of the Clinic was designed like this, with
massive glass areas that created a warm, almost
greenhouse-like atmosphere. The day had continued
bright and cloudless.

'Lovely, isn't it?' Roger mused, staring wistfully
over the landscape. 'You wouldn't believe that it was
freezing outside. Or that London was only an hour
away. Kent is such a beautiful county.' Roger, at fifty,
was a lot older than Gala, but she'd always got on well
with him—especially over this past year, now that she
was on the permanent staff. She nodded agreement
with his comments, and glanced over his shoulder at
the patients ploughing their way through the mighty
salads that were all most of them were allowed. There
was no sign of Conrad Brandon. No doubt he'd
ordered his meal served in his room, away from the
rabble. As though picking up her thoughts, Roger
dabbed his moustache with his napkin, and smiled at
her. 'How did you get on with Mr Brandon this
morning?'

'Not particularly well.' She snapped a crisp
breadroll moodily in half. 'He's an arrogant man.'

'Many successful men are,' Roger shrugged. 'Try
not to let it rile you. He's quite a hero with the
younger set, you know.'

For a second it occurred to her to tell Roger just
what a hero Con Brandon really was, but managed to
stifle the retort. 'What exactly *is* a rally?' she asked
instead.

'It's a sort of cross-country race, divided into stages.
Very gruelling, I understand.'

'I can believe that,' she said, frowning. 'He looks as

though he's been systematically pounded, Roger. It must be a hell of a way to make a living.'

'He doesn't have to rally.' Roger waved away the coffee the waitress was offering him, and leaned forward confidentially. 'Conrad Brandon's a very rich man in his own right. He owns a lot of real estate in London, and some very posh car showrooms, too. Rolls-Royces and Lamborghinis, that sort of thing.'

'Is that so?' Gala arched an eyebrow sardonically. Another reason for Crystal to have found him more attractive than Jack, who'd just been starting off as an architect then. Still, the man must be driven by some very special devils to compete so fiercely when he might be living a life of luxurious ease.

'Sure. Eligible batchelor numero uno. He's been causing quite a flutter of female hearts around here, I can tell you!'

'Freddie Griffiths will have to look to his laurels,' she replied lightly. She toyed idly with her food, and went on, 'Roger—do you ever let personal feelings interfere with your work?'

'You mean do I ever fall in love with young and beautiful patients?' he smiled.

'Actually, I meant rather the opposite.' She put her fork down and looked at him with a serious expression on her gentle mouth. 'Supposing you had some reason to really dislike a patient—maybe he'd run your dog over, or something like that. Anything. Would you be able to treat him like anyone else?'

'I hope so,' Roger nodded. 'Have you got that kind of problem with Conrad Brandon?'

'No,' she lied hastily. 'It was just—er—a thought.'

'Ah. Well, you soon learn to keep personal prejudice away from your work. I try and be the same benevolent old man to all my patients, whether I like them or not. It's best that way.'

'Yes,' Gala agreed, 'that's what I worked out, too.'

She picked up her knife and fork again, and attacked her lunch. That decision had hardened into a resolution. Her job was healing, and that was all there was to it. And Jack didn't even have to know that she was treating Brandon. She put him firmly out of her thoughts.

On her way back to her office, Gala bumped into the tall, thin figure of Richard Schwarzmuller. Her 'Oh, hello,' was rather flustered; the German-born doctor always made her a little nervous, not least because his good looks—aquiline with a thick black moustache—had a slightly sinister cast. She'd often felt his eyes on her, and though they didn't usually exchange more than the time of day, she had a shrewd feminine intuition that he was attracted to her.

'You must be very busy,' he smiled, steadying her.

'Just lost in my thoughts,' she said breathlessly.

'Not too lost to talk for five minutes, I hope?'

'Not at all.' Trying not to seem unwilling she let him lead her into his office. It was spotlessly tidy, even to the arrangement of his pens and pencils on the desk, and smelled, as all doctor's rooms seemed to, of meths. He waved her to a leather-upholstered swivel chair, and perched himself on the desk, folding his arms.

'Do you like the theatre?' he asked without preamble.

'The operating theatre?' she blinked.

'No,' he chuckled. 'The theatre as in Shakespeare.'

'Oh,' she said, feeling idiotic. 'Yes, very much. Why?'

'I have two tickets for *Hamlet* at the New Vic tomorrow night. My partner is unfortunately indisposed.' He smiled charmingly. 'I know it's very short notice, Gala, but would you like to come?'

'Oh——' Startled, Gala found herself lost for words.

'I'd be very honoured. I've always wanted to know you better. We are colleagues, after all, and it seems silly not to—how shall I put it? Improve our acquaintance.'

'I agree,' Gala said hastily. 'But I'm so sorry, Dr Schwarzmuller . . .'

'Please.' His eyes were the velvety brown of an alsatian's, really quite appealing. 'My name is Richard.'

'Richard,' she smiled guiltily. Would he, like an alsatian, be faithful and loyal? 'I promised to—er—go out with a friend tomorrow night. A girlfriend, I mean. I really am sorry.'

'It's quite all right. It *was* short notice, after all.'

'Sorry,' she said again, foolishly, and wondered why on earth she'd just refused him. He was personable, even handsome, and would probably be entertaining company.

'Maybe some other time, then,' he smiled.

'Oh yes!' Guilt at having lied to him made her over-pleased at the suggestion, and a look of pleasure crossed his thin face.

'You'd like that?' He groomed his moustache with quick, nervous movements. 'Then how about dinner some time?'

'Fine,' she nodded, determined not to turn him down again if she could help it. After all, she'd been working here for two years, and—either because she was so forbidding or the men here were so shy—he was the first remotely attractive man who'd asked her out!

'So. Maybe next week? Excellent. Perhaps you could give me a ring after the week-end and we'll arrange a time and a place?'

'I will,' she promised. She beamed at him as he ushered her out of his spotless office—and yet she was somehow relieved to be going. For all his charm, he simply wasn't her type, and she knew in her heart of hearts that dinner with him was going to be an effort.

Oh, come on! she muttered to herself as she hurried back to her next patient. Men aren't exactly queuing up to take you out. Give the guy a chance, can't you?

Thursday night was her squash night, and at five-thirty after work, Gala locked her office, and carried her kit-bag down to the squash-courts. The big building among the trees was deserted but for Alanna Cipriani, who was already waiting for her in one of the courts, swatting a ball patiently against the far wall. Gala waved hello from the spectator seats up above, and went round the back to change.

'How was your day?' Alanna asked as Gala came in, dressed in her usual white track-suit.

'Indifferent,' she smiled. 'How was yours?'

'Good. You under the weather or something?'

'Paying for last night's excesses,' Gala admitted. She wasn't exactly looking forward to the game, but she had to keep up her dedication to physical fitness. 'I had a bit too much to drink last night, and I'm still suffering.'

'That's not like you.' Alanna pulled off her own tracksuit bottom to reveal long, slim brown legs, and they started warming up. 'Were you celebrating something?'

'Mike was home on leave,' she nodded. 'He's just been made a senior pilot, so Jack and I helped him celebrate. He was tickled pink about it—the job, I mean.'

'I'll bet.' Alanna slammed the ball along the side wall. 'He works for one of the Scandinavian airlines, doesn't he?'

'Yes.'

'He's very young to have made senior pilot already.'

'You were a doctor at twenty-three,' Gala pointed out with a smile. 'Besides, Mike's a brilliant flier.' She

stooped to pick up a ball she'd missed. Alanna
watched her affectionately. She was a few years older
than Gala, a slim woman with a round, dark-eyed face
which sparkled with humour. They'd liked each other
from the first, when Gala joined the Clinic two years
ago, and though their work was a long way apart—
Alanna was involved with the research into glandular
disorders which was one of the Clinic's important
side-lines—they met regularly on the squash court or
after hours.

'You adore your brothers, don't you?' she asked.
Gala simply nodded. Mike and Jack were large,
handsome men who'd always let their kid sister join in
their games, and the three of them were very close.
Almost closer, she sometimes thought, than they were
to their parents. And towards Jack, inwardly vulnerable despite his athletic exterior, she felt a fiercely
protective love.

'Richard Schwarzmuller asked me out this afternoon,' she told Alanna. Alanna's slender brows
arched.

'Not bad. He's very good-looking.'

'You think so? Anyway, I had to turn him down,
but he's taking me to dinner sometime next week.'

'Very nice,' Alanna nodded approvingly. 'Very nice
indeed. Nice *going*. You could do worse, you know.'

'What?' Gala laughed, amused. 'Than marry him?
He's only asked me to dinner, Alanna.'

'If he was an Englishman, yes.' Alanna squeezed a
squash-ball reflectively. 'But you have to understand
your nationalities. Germans are very serious people,
you know. If Richard asked you out, it's a bet that he's
been watching you for some time. He's definitely
interested, or he wouldn't have bothered.'

'Are you kidding me?' Gala's distressed expression
made her partner grin.

'Well, I'm half-serious. He's a nice guy, really. And

a very good doctor. Very thorough.' Her dark eyes danced with wicked mischief. '*Very* thorough. An excellent sign in a prospective lover!'

'Disgusting woman,' Gala said reprovingly. 'I refuse to listen anymore.' She swatted the ball high against the wall, making Alanna scramble for it. 'Okay,' she panted after a few more minutes of warming-up, 'let's play.'

The game, like all their games, was hard-fought, though they were very different kinds of player. Alanna could hit the ball surprisingly hard, and her long legs carried her swiftly around the court; but she lacked Gala's lightning ability to think one move ahead, and Gala could catch her with the same ruses time and again.

'You're just *sneaky*!' Alanna gasped as she lunged hopelessly after a ball Gala had flicked into the corner. Exertion had them both pink and perspiring.

'Skilled, you mean,' Gala laughed breathlessly. Her game was deceptively graceful, but cost her a lot in terms of co-ordination and concentration.

'Low animal cunning, I call it. Your point, I think.'

'As a physiotherapist, I wouldn't recommend my worst enemy to play this game,' Gala said ruefully as they walked back to their squares. She wiped sweat off her eyebrows. 'I've seen more wrenched knees and sprained ankles from squash than any other sport. However . . .' She served the ball hard into the nearside corner, '. . . I suppose we both need the exercise.'

They played the next game in silence. The tiredness of the day had slipped off Gala now, and she was enjoying the challenge to her body and wits. It was good to extend herself, to stretch muscles and mind, feel the whole system working perfectly together. Still, she was dripping by the end of their last game, which Alanna managed to win, and glad to stop and get her breath back.

'Well played,' she panted, snatching up her towel and draping it over her head. 'Whew! You were full of energy tonight!'

'I was just taking advantage of your hangover,' Alanna said smugly.

'I feel I've atoned a bit now, anyway.' Gala towelled her flushed face. 'This is supposed to get the poisons out of your system, isn't it? In more senses than one.'

'What does that mean?' Alanna smiled.

'Oh—something rather depressing cropped up during the day, and I've only just shaken it off.' She picked up her racket, feeling like talking to Alanna about Crystal and Jack, and for some reason glanced upwards. Someone was sitting in the darkened auditorium above. With an unpleasant shock she recognised Conrad Brandon. He was leaning back in one of the centre seats, legs crossed and arms stretched out along the seats beside him. Gala's face tightened. How long had he been watching? It was too dark to see the expression on his face, but he was wearing dark slacks and a dark pullover. Alanna followed her gaze upwards, and waved cheerfully.

'Hi, Con! How are you making out?'

'Not bad.' He got up, and walked down the centre aisle to learn on the railing over their heads. 'They seem to think I'm a rabbit, though. They won't let me eat anything except lettuce.'

Alanna giggled. 'And no alcohol, either, you poor thing.'

'At least it's peaceful here.' The cloudy eyes flicked to Gala, who was standing silently watching them, her face still cupped in her towel. Where did Alanna know this man from? It wasn't a coincidence she found amusing. That sense of depression, of disturbance, was firmly in place again. She didn't feel at her best in a clammy track-suit, her face no doubt scarlet and sweaty, being looked down on by that cool, yet somehow lambent gaze.

'I'm going to shower, Alanna,' she said, unable to keep the stiffness out of her voice.

'Stay and meet Con Brandon,' Alanna smiled. 'Con, this is Gala Fletcher . . .'

'We've already met,' Gala interrupted, her smile just a ritual. She didn't look up at the dark, saturnine face above. 'Excuse me.' She picked up her kit bag, and pushed her way through the doorway at the back of the court. Her reaction was childish, she knew, but she couldn't help it. She simply didn't like the man, and she didn't like being watched by him. She slammed the door on what she knew was going to be a surprised—and most likely amused—silence behind her.

CHAPTER TWO

A SHEAF of files was waiting on her desk the next morning. The first one was Conrad Brandon's. Dripping wet from the pouring rain that had settled in overnight, she picked it up, and flipped it open, thinking uncomfortably of her stupid behaviour last night. Forgetting who Conrad Brandon was wasn't going to be that easy. The notes inside, in Lionel Parker's erratic scrawl, contained little that she hadn't already worked out for herself. *Mr Brandon habitually drives himself to excel*, the report concluded. *Despite an iron will and an inherently strong constitution, he shows signs of mental and physical strain. In particular, he would benefit from traction to ease muscular spasms caused by prolapsed intervertebral discs, and a period of intense rest.* There followed a chart of personal details like blood-pressure and pulse rates which she postponed reading till later.

Gala closed the file, and pulled off her raincoat. Had she made a complete fool of herself yesterday? Alanna hadn't commented on her brusqueness towards Conrad Brandon when she'd joined her in the shower a few minutes after Gala had walked out. She'd simply mentioned that she and Con Brandon were old friends. That had effectively silenced Gala's intentions of telling Alanna about Jack and Crystal, and they'd showered in silence. Brandon had probably told Alanna about her aggressive attitude that morning. Yes, she *had* made a fool of herself. She bit her lip. She tried hard to be professional in all her dealings with patients, and she was cursing herself for having allowed a personal dislike to put her off her stride so badly.

Impulsively, she opened the file again, and ran her eyes down the page. His age was given as 34. Maybe that was part of it—the instinctive wariness between people separated by ten years. She'd only been working for two years, and before that she'd been at a college, doing her diploma—and he had the arrogant assurance of someone who'd climbed to the very top of his profession.

'Oh, dear,' she sighed softly. Her insecurities were showing through, it seemed. Even though she'd done well in her probationary year, and was now on the permanent staff, she still felt absurdly young sometimes. Her eldest brother Michael was well on his way to becoming a top pilot. Jack, only a few years older than herself, was a highly talented architect establishing a fine reputation with a prestigious firm in London. *Her* only gift seemed to be a rather nebulous ability to heal—an ability which she knew was only beginning to be developed. Well, it was time to start excercising that gift—she was due to take a class of handicapped children in two minutes. She changed into her smock, and hurried off to the exercise room.

The session, as always, was both painful and rewarding. The five children were brought in to the Clinic by their parents every second week (Gala drove out to each of their houses for individual sessions every other week) where they could take advantage of the special equipment available. It wasn't always pleasant urging the children to extend themselves in the necessary exercises, which could be very painful; but without them, Gala knew, many of the children faced total loss of movement.

'Which is why,' she reminded Sonia McRae gently, 'it isn't really a kindness to excuse them when the going gets tough.' Sonia met Gala's eyes guiltily, grimaced, and nodded understanding.

'I know. It's just so *hard . . .*'

'Hard, but worth it. Let me help.' Gala leaned forward and gritted her teeth as they tried to get Tarquin, Mrs McRae's paraplegic son, to haul himself upright on the special frame. She knew how vital it was to keep the muscles working and in co-ordination; but it *was* hard. Sometimes agonisingly so, like now, when Tarquin's eyes filled with tears.

'I suppose this is called being cruel to be kind,' Sonia sighed. 'Come on, son.'

Gala found herself wondering suddenly how *she* would react with a son like Tarquin. Would she have the courage to see it through, the courage to bear not only her own pain but her child's?

'It must take someone very special,' she whispered, almost to herself.

'Not special.' Sonia had heard the words. 'Just realistic.' She met Gala's deep green eyes, and smiled faintly.

At the end of the class, in the general hubbub of packing up, something caught Gala's eye. It was a comic brought in by one of the children. On the glossy back page was a row of photographs, captioned 'Rally Stars'. She picked it up curiously. Conrad Brandon's picture was given pride of place—'British champion twice running'. The white helmet he was wearing almost covered his face. Only those smoky eyes and a glimpse of tanned cheek were visible under the visor. She looked down at the garish illustration beneath. A fast-looking car, plastered with decals and brand-names, performing an impossibly sharp turn in the midst of a cloud of red dust.

'That's Tarquin's.' Sonia McRae came up with her arm around her boy. 'He's mad about anything noisy—like sports cars. Sorry—he leaves everything lying around, Gala.' Gala gave the comic back to the child, a wry expression settling gently on her mouth. It seemed she was bumping into Conrad Brandon at every turn, whether she wanted to or not. It was strange to have a patient who was so famous. A patient she had such strong feelings about. Habitually, she glanced at her watch. And who was coming in for his first treatment later on this morning. Her heart sank dully at the thought.

A combination of tension and dislike helped to make her doubly stiff by the time his appointment was due. And she was disgusted to find that her heart was pounding hard as he walked into her office. Again, he was wearing dark slacks and a beautiful and clearly expensive grey sweater, a stag embroidered over his heart. He was almost diabolically handsome. Black brows, eyes the colour of a winter fjord, the mahogany of his skin shading into the stubble of a beard over the lean curves of jaw and chin—it was a stunning combination. Like a gas furnace, that flash of inner disturbance ignited dislike inside Gala. She rose to meet him, feeling her face go as expressionless as a board.

'I trust I'm not late this time?' he said coolly. Only the glint in his eyes suggested that he hadn't forgotten her antagonism towards him yesterday.

'Good morning, Mr Brandon. I'd like to begin right away, please.' Sounding as officious as she knew how, Gala indicated the couch. 'I'd like you to sit on the edge of that.'

He didn't move to obey. Tall and ultra-male, he leaned against the door with folded arms, his dark eyes brooding on her.

'Ms Fletcher . . .' The accent on the *Ms* was just short of insulting. '. . . my bed was changed by the staff yesterday. When I got into it, I found they'd put a kind of plank into it. And there was only one pillow. When I called Reception about it, they told me this was on your specific instructions.'

'That's right.' She waited tensely.

'I know you don't like me,' he said, his eyebrows lowering, 'but surely this is simply childish spite?'

'Spite?' Gala stared back, wide-eyed in surprise.

'Or perhaps your idea of a joke?' he suggested. 'You don't seriously mean to tell me that there's any medical benefit from ruining what little sleep I already get?'

'I'm sorry,' Gala said coldly. 'They ought to have explained when they put the fracture-board on your bed. It's essential in the case of lumbar disc lesions, and quite common practice, I assure you.'

'Really?' His quirked eyebrow expressed arrogant disbelief.

'Yes, really.' Anger put a glint of green ice in her eyes. 'You're in urgent need of treatment, Mr Brandon. You don't seem to realise how badly you've treated your own body.'

'It hasn't affected my driving,' he said grimly.

'I don't believe that.' The words came out cold and precise. She stared back into the arctic hostility of those grey-blue eyes. 'I think that's exactly what's happened. The injuries you've been building up for years have finally started affecting the one thing that matters a damn to you—your precious driving. Nothing else would have brought you here!'

'What insight. You're quite a Gypsy Rose.' But for all his cool poise, he didn't contradict her.

'Yes. And I'll tell you something else, Mr Brandon. I'll bet you're afraid. And that fear, as much as pain, stops you from sleeping.'

He laughed gently, teeth glinting white against tanned, ironic lips. 'So. And what am I afraid of—*Ms* Fletcher?'

She took a deep breath, determined to get behind that hateful façade of his.

'You're afraid because you've started to limp.

Sometimes your legs feel numb, and sometimes you get sharp pains from your back into your legs. You can't run as far as you used to, sometimes you feel you can hardly walk. It's getting worse, too. All the time. And that makes you most afraid of all.'

His eyes had narrowed to impenetrable slits, and she could see the tautness of his shoulder muscles under the fine cashmere.

'You sound very positive,' he rasped.

'I am positive.' She had obviously touched some inner target in the man, but she wasn't sure whether to be triumphant or afraid. 'You look pretty fit,' she went on, watching him speculatively. 'Can you touch your toes?'

'Of course.'

'Show me,' she invited. After a second's hesitation, he shrugged, put his heels together, and reached down. Six inches from the floor, his square brown hands halted. She sensed the effort he was making, and saw the quiver of strained muscles. The hands stayed where they were. He drew himself slowly upright. There was a dull film of pain over the brightness of his gaze. 'That isn't just stiffness, Mr Brandon,' she said gently. 'Lie on the couch, and lift your right leg straight up, please.'

Again, he paused before doing what she'd asked. Then he lay back, his face expressionless, and she saw his stomach muscles come into relief under the cashmere. His leg didn't move. With a silent snarl, he dug his fingers into the couch, and poured energy into the effort. Sweat sheened suddenly on his brow, and his whole body shook with the attempt. Formidably powerful as he was, Gala knew that those honed muscles were fighting damaged and paralysed nerves, and that the battle was hopeless. His leg lifted with agonised slowness. A few inches above the couch it collapsed. Conrad Brandon slumped into immobility, staring up at the ceiling with a contained fury that almost frightened Gala.

'Do you believe me now?' she asked in a level voice. She didn't have any pity to spare for him, but she didn't want mutual dislike to get in the way of her work any more, either. 'You aren't going to end up paralysed, Mr Brandon. Not unless you're stubborn. Or stupid. Or both. With a few weeks of treatment, you'll be free of pain and all the other symptoms of the pressure on those nerves. I don't know how you've done that to your back—I'd guess by driving fast over rough ground, or maybe in one or more crashes—but it's going to take time and co-operation to heal.' With the triumphant feeling that she'd made her point, she walked over to the traction machine, and wheeled it over to the couch where he lay. She'd taken a cold pleasure in seeing him humbled. She remembered the weeks of depression, of bitter humiliation, that Jack had gone through. Maybe now Mr bloody Brandon wouldn't be quite so arrogant! She took his arm firmly in both hands, and helped to pull him upright.

'Could you take your sweater off, please?' she asked.

His eyes met hers, lines of pain still haunting their edges.

'You enjoyed that,' he said softly. She froze for a second, then folded her arms.

'I don't know what you mean,' she said briskly.

'And I wonder just what makes you react towards me like this,' he said in the same quiet voice. She couldn't meet his eyes, and looked away with flushed cheeks. 'You obviously have some reason to dislike me very strongly, Ms Fletcher. Would you mind telling me what it is?'

'There is no reason,' she snapped, but the rising note in her own voice gave the lie to her statement.

'Very well.' His face hardened into a cold mask.

'There is no reason. Shall we get on with the exercises?'

Alanna Cipriani's car had broken down that week for the umpteenth time, and Gala gave her a lift back to London after work on Friday night.

'It's the alternator,' Alanna complained as they drove through the extensive grounds of the Clinic towards the main road. 'So they tell me. The blasted thing *would* have to give up the ghost in this.' She glared out at the whirling snow that was obviously settling in for the week-end. The headlights of Gala's elderly Morris Ital poked their way cautiously through the thick curtain of heavy white flakes.

'Hmm. I don't know if I'm going to be able to get in tomorrow,' Gala sighed. The Clinic was fairly remote from the nearest bus or train services, and without a car, getting there could be a problem. 'If it gets any heavier I'll have to ask Roger to pick us up—that old Land-Rover of his will get through just about anything.'

Alanna huddled into her overcoat. The Ital's heating wasn't exactly tropical. 'How are you getting on with Con Brandon?' she asked casually. Gala spared her a glance, but her friend's face was calm in the ghostly light from the snow.

'All right,' she said guardedly.

'That's good.'

'His treatment's pretty conservative,' Gala said, feeling she had to say something. 'Mainly rest, and gentle back extension exercises two or three times a day. He doesn't need a lumbro-sacral support or anything.' She drove carefully on to the main road through the big stone gates. The fresh snow was making the road dangerously treacherous. 'He'll be back behind the wheel in no time.'

'Good,' Alanna said again. 'I was really sorry to see

him arrive at the Clinic. I hate the thought of his being hurt. He's an amazing man, you know. I was more than half in love with him for ages.'

'Really. It's a small world.' The dry answer brought a slight smile to Alanna's lips.

'You don't like him one little bit.' It was a statement, not a question, and Gala didn't say anything. Alanna lay back in her seat, still smiling. 'Con taught me to drive when I was seventeen, years and years ago. He was living just around the corner from my parents' house then, in this lovely ramshackle old cottage by the river. I thought he was the most wonderful man I'd ever seen.' Her voice dropped to a soft flutter. 'Sometimes I still think so. But he was a hard teacher. He was a brilliant driver, of course. He could make a car do tricks. Bikes, too. I used to beg him to do wheelies down the strip, like some street cowboy. Fancy that—the future British champion roaring down the avenue on a Harley with a teenage kid clinging round his waist. I got through my driving-test first time, though.'

'That's nice,' Gala said expressionlessly.

'On my eighteenth birthday he took me for my first legal drink at the local pub.' Alanna giggled reminiscently. 'A Pink Lady. Horrible stuff, but I thought it was delicious. Con represented everything that was delicious—and forbidden.' She glanced at Gala. 'Alcohol, fast cars, sex . . .'

'Sex?' Gala repeated sharply.

'Don't bite my head off,' her friend smiled. 'He's the sexiest man in the world. Or hadn't you noticed?' She sighed. 'Not that he ever did anything to me, so take that prim look off your face, Galatea Fletcher.'

The use of her full name suddenly brought back a fleeting memory of Brian. He'd called her Galatea from the first time they'd met. And Brian had taught her to drive, in the cloud-blue Rolls-Royce that was carrying him on his single-minded path to wealth and success. Had Alanna felt about Con Brandon the way she'd felt about Brian Matthews? 'How moral of him,' she said coolly, in response to Alanna's last statement.

'Yes,' Alanna said regretfully. 'And it wasn't for lack of trying on my part, either. But he was six or seven years older than me, and I guess he just didn't notice my wiles. Besides, he just had to lift an eyebrow to get women running to him. I used to go and watch him rally whenever I could. God, he was beautiful! The most gorgeous man in any crowd. Women used to flock round him, like something out of a Hollywood picture. I've still got an empty magnum of champagne from one of his victories. And then he made a fortune out of his car business, and started buying hotels and ships and things.' She sighed again. 'The ramshackle old cottage fetched a hundred thousand—that had been a brilliant investment, too—and he bought himself a mansion somewhere posh—Kew, I think. He had an affair with an Italian Princess, too. It was at that stage,' she said with a touch of irony, wiping a patch clean on her window and peering out into the driving snowstorm, 'that I realised I was a long way out of Con's league. Are you sure we're going in the right direction?'

'Positive,' Gala said. She'd been fascinated by Alanna's reminiscences, even though it was practically impossible to square this rosy portrait with her own knowledge of the man. 'So you're still friends?'

'Yes. I'll always be Con's friend.' She put on a whining Cockney voice. ''E wos werry good to me, 'e wos. Dickens,' she said in answer to Gala's interrogatory eyebrow. 'I was always a bit of a waif, and Con looked after me like a guardian angel. For a while I cherished a hope that when I was all growed up, and a doctor and whatnot, Con might take a bit more interest in me. Red-roses-and-champagne sort of interest, I mean.'

'But he didn't?' Gala supplied.

'No such luck. I'm still his surrogate kid sister.'

They were joining the motorway near Sevenoaks now, and conditions were a lot better. For one thing, the road had been gritted, and there wasn't that horribly slidy feel to the steering now. They dropped easily into another topic of conversation, as though Alanna sensed that she wasn't in the mood to talk about Conrad Brandon. But as Gala pulled up in the snowy street outside Alanna's shared house in Purley, Alanna turned to her.

'Gala—I'm really sorry you aren't getting on with Conrad.'

'Did he tell you that?' she asked sharply. Their sessions had been spent in frigid silence so far, and she hadn't even bothered to disguise her dislike of the rally-driver any more.

'He didn't need to tell me,' Alanna said gently. 'It's painfully obvious. What have you got against the man, Gala? He hasn't done anything to you. Or has he?'

'I really don't want to talk about it,' Gala said coldly.

'Oh, come on! You're talking like a heroine in some Victorian melodrama. I know you're supposed to be the Ice Princess, but this is plain silly.'

'What do you mean, Ice Princess?' Gala asked in puzzlement.

'Oh, didn't you know?' Alanna looked discomforted. 'That's what some of the doctors call you. A kind of nickname.'

'I see,' Gala said, anger burning in her.

'It's not meant nastily,' Alanna hurried on. 'It's more of an affectionate tribute, really. Because you're so efficient, so . . .'

'So cold,' Gala supplied tersely. So they made jokes

about her, did they? Just because she didn't join in the wife-swapping free-swinging round that some of them considered so chic!

'Forget I said that, anyway,' Alanna went on. 'We were talking about Con Brandon. He's your patient, after all—and it's practically unethical to treat him the way you do.'

'I don't need a lecture on professional ethics, thanks,' Gala retorted. For the first time in their friendship, she was on the verge of a really furious quarrel with Alanna, and her stomach was tense with nerves. 'Look, Alanna, drop it, *please*.'

'I know you think it's none of my business,' Alanna said gently, 'but you're both good friends of mine, and I hate to see this dislike between you, whatever its cause. Look—if Con made a pass at you, and I don't know whether he did or not, I can understand that you might be upset. But aren't you taking this to extremes?'

'Has he asked you to act as ambassadress?' Gala asked angrily.

'Of course not . . .'

'Then stay out of this! You don't know what it's all about, and I don't want to tell you.' For a second Gala wondered furiously how Alanna would react if she knew how her precious Con had wrecked her brother's life, humiliated Jack, humiliated her parents. 'I realise that he's your idol, but if you want to know how I feel about him, he's a callous, destructive man who's done a great deal of harm. No matter how kindly he's treated you or anyone else. I hope he recovers as soon as possible—because I don't want him in my surgery any more than necessary! And you can tell him that!'

'He didn't send me,' Alanna said in a quiet voice. 'Con Brandon doesn't need me to represent him. And if you think I'd repeat any part of this conversation to anyone else, you don't know me. Goodnight, Gala.'

She got out, closed the door, and walked quickly across the whitened street to her front door.

'Damn!' Still shaking with anger, Gala cursed herself for losing control yet again, and slammed the car into gear.

She was a lot colder—and a lot more miserable—by the time she got back to her own flat. The quiet Wandsworth street was a strange mixture—a beautiful old Georgian terrace on one side, facing a modern Leech development on the other. She was lucky enough to have got the whole top floor of one of the Georgian houses two years ago, and she'd been blissfully happy here ever since.

The central heating whispered into life just as she closed the door behind her, starting to take the chill off the air. The first thing she did was to pick up the telephone and dial Alanna.

'Hello,' she said in a small voice. 'I'm sorry.'

'Don't be silly.' Alanna's laugh was warm. 'I was way out of line. My well-meaning bumbling has always got me into trouble. I won't bring the subject up again. Okay?'

'You weren't bumbling. And I was a wasp. I'd hate this to come between us.'

'It won't,' Alanna promised. 'But if you ever feel like telling me exactly what it is you've got against Con, I'd be very interested.'

'When he's left the Clinic,' Gala said, 'maybe . . .'

'In your own time. It's just that you're both my friends, see?'

'I do see. We just have different views of him.'

'And mine's a very rosy one. I know. Look, don't mind that Ice Princess stuff. You know half of them are simply dying to get into your pants.'

'A charming turn of phrase,' Gala smiled. 'No, I don't mind it.'

'Good. Get some hot cocoa into you, kiddo. I'm

having some, and it warms the cockles.' A contented slurping sound came down the line to illustrate. 'Will you ring me early tomorrow about a lift?'

'Of course. Sleep well. Goodnight, Alanna.'

She put the receiver down. At the same time there was a soft click and a miaow as Pasha pushed her way through her private entrance at the kitchen door. The fluffy grey cat who was her sole flatmate leapt up on to her shoulder in an ecstasy of purring.

'Hello,' Gala smiled, scratching the little round head. 'What have you been doing today?' Pasha's affectionate kneading, as always, was too much to bear, and she lifted the fluffy bundle into her arms. That advice about cocoa sounded good. She went through to her spotless kitchen put the kettle on, and poured Pasha a saucer of milk. She couldn't help looking around with a smug feeling of pride. She'd had a new set of pine units installed at the end of last year. A kind of statement of her independence, her permanence here. Her parents' house in Tunbridge Wells was lovely, an old Jacobean farmhouse that had been lovingly restored; but she cherished her independence in London.

She ran her fingers lovingly over the gleaming wood. It was made with the sort of fine craftsman-ship she admired. And with the cooker she'd bought eight months ago, and the nearly-new washing-mach-ine her parents had given her for her last birthday, the kitchen was definitely looking up! Getting a mortgage to buy the flat hadn't been that difficult. She was almost well-paid, and though the place had been rather a mess when she'd taken it over—it had been a sort of communal pad for decades of bohemian students—she'd made it as beautiful as she could afford. Only the bathroom, with its horrible 1960s' vinyl wallpaper and its poster of John Lennon over the hole in the plaster, was still in the original condition. And as soon as spring arrived, she was going to do that up, too.

Downstairs lived a retired couple, and above her was a spacious loft, her own property, which she had plans for sometime. It was quiet, and the proportions of the rooms had an elegance, a grandeur, that belonged to a bygone age. One day she'd be able to afford the furniture the flat deserved.

Thinking about Alanna, she started making a simple dinner out of eggs and bacon. Her dark-eyed friend was obviously in love with Con Brandon. Detached opinions weren't to be expected from her. But no matter how fond she was of Alanna Cipriani, Gala wasn't about to forget what Brandon had done to Jack. If Alanna hadn't turned out to be such a fan of Con's, she might have been able to talk to her about him. But as it was . . .

She and Con had hardly exchanged more than two words that afternoon, not even when she'd massaged the locked muscles of his back, her palms pressing carefully into the teak-hard muscles. His skin had been sun-warm again, as fine as velvet under her palms. She could smell the sunshine on him. And beneath that, an elusive masculine musk.

It was easy to recall his face to her mind's eye. Perilously easy. A mature face, the silver at his temples adding calm to the untamed fire that glinted in his eyes and in the shadows of his mouth.

She scuffled the eggs and bacon into a messy omelette, a dish she'd enjoyed since childhood, and took it through to eat it on the sofa with Pasha in front of the early evening news. The world was unusually peaceful tonight, it seemed. The girl who did the weather report, a beautiful brunette, was wearing her hair in a thick braid that came over her shoulder. Gala hadn't had her hair cut for a long time, and it was just about long enough to go into a braid like that.

Pasha got the left-overs of her dinner as a treat. Later, she washed her hair and dried it, and tried it out in a plait. It took half an hour, but when it was done she could lay it across the creamy skin of her naked shoulder like a cable of burnished copper. It looked different. Striking. Maybe she'd wear it like this tomorrow.

Gala Fletcher stared at her own face in the mirror. The soft shadows in her cheeks and around her mouth had always given her a look of Vivien Leigh. A younger, fairer, happier Vivien Leigh, vulnerable and yet unwounded. Sorrow would write easily in that face, leaving marks that would be impossible to hide. She'd have to avoid it. If she could. Her colouring, she'd long since decided, was definitely autumnal— hair the colour of dying leaves, or sunsets, and eyes that held the cool depth of a forest pool. Did Richard Schwarzmuller think her beautiful? And Con Brandon? Was he attracted to her?

Neither youth nor beauty lasted long, she thought on a sudden shaft of melancholy. The flat was silent. Ice Princess? That wasn't really very funny. Was she really cold? Maybe it was time she made a conscious effort to fall in love.

'Miaow?' Pasha's enquiring face looked up at her, adoring yellow eyes wanting to know how late she intended to stay up staring at her own face in the mirror.

She went to bed with *Orthopaedic and Neurosurgical Emergencies*, and stared at the pages, dreamily stroking Pasha's soft fur and listening to her purring.

CHAPTER THREE

THE improvement in Con was obvious, even in the way he held himself. The limp was almost gone, and he moved with an elemental grace that made her hold her breath, despite all her antagonism. If he hadn't been a racing driver, she thought, he might have been anything he chose. There was a power in him that seemed to radiate from deep inside, like the energy in a nuclear reactor. And in common with the very few other truly strong men Gala had known, his physical strength seemed to be rooted in the centre of his body, in the stomach muscles that could clench into steel hardness; in the supple co-ordination of thighs and loins.

Wearing only black briefs, Conrad Brandon was lying on the floor of her surgery, doing slow sit-ups while she held his ankles.

'Keep your back absolutely straight,' she said in a level voice. It was hard not to be hypnotised by the sheer beauty of his body. Like Pasha, he moved with an utter lack of self-consciousness. Like a dancer. 'That'll do,' she decided, rising from her kneeling position. He relaxed for a second, then rose with uncramped, economical movements.

'You're quite good,' he said in his quiet, deep voice. 'And I take back my complaints about the bed.'

'You feel better?' she queried.

'Much. I don't get headaches any more. And the numbness in my legs has almost disappeared.'

'Good.' She couldn't help the slight smile of satisfaction that tugged at her soft mouth. It wasn't meant for him, but his brooding eyes hadn't missed it.

'Well, well. I was beginning to wonder whether you didn't have a slight case of paralysis as well.'

'Paralysis?' she echoed.

'Of the *orbicularis oris*.' He slid himself into his wine-red gown, tying the sash around his lean waist. 'The cheek-muscles,' he said drily in response to her rapid blinking. 'Used in smiling.'

Gala turned away, no ready answer springing to her rescue. She picked up his file. 'You won't need to stay here much longer, Mr Brandon,' she said flatly. 'If you just keep up the exercise and take it easy, there's no reason why you shouldn't be discharged in a few days.'

'And leave you in peace.' He slid his hands into his pockets, watching her from under level black brows. 'I'm sorry to have upset your tidy little applecart, Gala.' The use of her first name snapped her head round to look at him—and be scalded in the grey fire of his gaze. 'Here you were, tranquil and happy, and along I had to come with my bad back and blot up all your sunshine.' He gestured at the window, where snow was still flurrying. 'I even brought the snow, yes?'

'Are you trying to make some point?' she asked witheringly.

'No. But you've been trying to make one ever since I arrived here.'

'I'm not aware of that,' she said, her heart beginning to beat unsteadily. Inconsequentially, she noticed that he had the longest eyelashes she'd ever seen on a man, a dark cover which he could use to deadly effect to unleash the ambush of his truly startling gaze.

'Come on.' The rasp in his voice made her jump slightly. 'You've been treating me like a rattlesnake, Gala. You hate my being here, you absolutely loathe having to touch my skin—have I got some wicked aura that you think will rub off on you?'

'Let's put it this way,' she snapped, tired of concealment, 'you didn't exactly come to me with shining recommendations.'

'And what the hell does that mean?' he demanded, eyes narrowed.

'Nothing,' she bit out. Telling him she was Jack's sister would only worsen the problem a hundredfold.

'Nothing?' he repeated dangerously. 'Someone's obviously given you some tittle-tattle about me. What is it? Some girl I'm supposed to have seduced?'

'Your treatment is over,' she said frigidly, wishing he knew just how close he was to the truth. 'You can go now.'

'Damn you!' He moved towards her with frightening speed. 'Don't you dare talk to me like that, girl!'

'If you don't let me go,' she panted, white-faced and really afraid that he might hurt her, 'I'll scream.'

'Scream your pretty head off, then. It's time you grew up, Gala Fletcher.' His eyes dropped in an insolent survey of her breasts, straining against the front of her smock. 'Your body's adult, but your mind's still in bloomers.'

'I'm not as childish as you'd like to think,' she hissed. 'I understand you all too well, Mr Brandon.'

'Well I damn well don't understand you,' he retorted. 'What the hell *have* you got against me?'

'Look back over your past sins,' she sneered, 'and pick the most suitable one.'

'Are you really trying to make me angry?' he asked in a voice that curdled her blood. A vein was pulsing in the bronzed column of his throat, and she stared at it in numbed fascination. His grip was hard enough to cut the blood supply off to her hands, making them tingle. He stared down at her with unveiled contempt. 'I don't know what I'm doing, trying to communicate with you,' he grated. 'I don't owe you any apologies, Gala. And you won't get any, ever.' Her knees, weak with nerves and emotional strain, buckled without warning, and she toppled against him helplessly. His body was hard againt hers, her open mouth so close to his that for a second she felt his warm breath on her lips. Then he pushed her away in disgust. 'Is that what this is all about? I might have known. Try it again when you've grown up—*Miz* Fletcher.'

He slammed the door hard as he walked out of her office, and Gala slumped into her chair, fighting back the sobs. The bastard! The final, unsupportable insult had been his assumption that she wanted him to kiss her. The cold, conceited *swine*! She wiped the tears furiously off her lids, and blew her nose hard into a tissue. Well, that was the last straw. She wasn't going to treat Conrad Brandon ever again. She'd see him in hell first. Let Roger Trefusis handle his case—Roger was such an expert at keeping his feelings separate from his work, wasn't he?

She didn't even have time for the luxury of a good cry. There was a tap at the door within seconds of Con leaving. Mrs Neill, as always, was impatient for her physiotherapy. Gala got up wearily to deal with her. The world had to go on, and Mrs Neill was only concerned about her arthritis. She came in with her usual catalogue of aches and pains. If she noticed Gala's red eyes and swollen lids, she had either too much discretion or too little curiosity to make any comment.

Gala got into her Morris after lunch, feeling tired and ill. Thank God it was her half-day. She'd promised her parents she'd visit them this afternoon, but her fight with Con had decided her to spend the rest of the day in bed instead. She drove down the private road through the park, only half-aware of the beauty of the trees, their branches intricately filigreed with snow. The whole world was white, the woods white on white all around her. Only the road, churned into slush by the wheels of staff and patients' cars, was a dirty yellow. Down the bank, past the squash courts, she felt the car slide perilously on a bend. It was unpleasantly slippery, and she was going to have to be careful all the way home. Maybe she shouldn't have risked driving her own car. She should have accepted that lift in Roger's Land-Rover.

She barely crawled for the next mile, until the Clinic's wide gates were in sight. Then she accelerated down the hill that led to the main road. It was a bad mistake. Again, she felt the rear wheels lose their grip, but this time the slide didn't correct itself. She swung the wheel jerkily, worsening the skid. Cursing herself helplessly, she could only cling to the wheel as the car turned along its own length in the road, picking up speed fast as it turned 180 degrees, and slammed into a deep drift of snow halfway down the hill, knocking the breath out of her lungs.

In a miserable silence, she slumped wearily over the wheel, almost wishing she'd been killed. It had been a ghastly day. The windscreen was buried in snow, and the engine was ominously dead. She sat in a blank trance for several minutes. Suddenly the door was jerked open.

'Are you all right?' She looked up dully to see Conrad Brandon's tense face. It would have to be him.

'I'm okay,' she said in a tired voice. 'I skidded on the snow.'

'I know.' He reached around her to unbuckle her seatbelt. 'I saw you. You drive like a farmer pushing a wheelbarrow.' He helped her out, and slid into the driver's seat himself. Gala stood in the road like a glum snowman, watching him as he restarted the engine and backed the little orange car out of the drift. Plastered with snow, one headlight rakishly dented, the car looked ridiculously like a mournful clown-face doing some barbershop joke with shaving cream.

He stopped the car, and slid out, holding the door open for her. 'Get in,' he commanded. 'I'm going to show you what to do in a skid.'

'I don't feel like driving just yet,' she said pettishly. 'I could have killed myself there . . .'

'Which is why I want to teach you how not to kill yourself in future,' he interrupted. He pushed her firmly into the driver's seat, walked round the car, and got in beside her. His big male presence dwarfed the car's interior. 'You've got to know how to control a skid if you want to drive in snow. Drive on,' he ordered.

'No,' she said, hearing her own voice whinge like a child's. 'I'm not well . . .'

'*Move.*' The whiplash command had her reaching for the gearstick in panic. What it was about him that made her obey was hard to pin down, but she didn't dare contradict him. She set off down the hill again, feeling distinctly unhappy. 'Faster,' he ordered. 'Okay, brace yourself.' He reached for the wheel with one hand. 'This is called a rear wheel skid.' He pulled the wheel sharply down, and the rear wheels immediately spun out of control with horrible familiarity. Gala screamed as the car started turning on its own axis, just as it had done minutes ago. 'And this is how to correct it,' he said quietly. With surprising gentleness he steered the car into the skid, squaring up the front and back wheels. Suddenly, the car was rolling forward again—at an angle across the road, but under its own control. 'Brake,' he told her. 'Gently.' He straightened the Ital out at the edge of the road and they came to a gentle halt. 'Now,' he said, eyes probing hers, 'you try it.'

'Supposing I crash again?' she asked, her foot shaking on the clutch as she set off. It struck her that just after an accident wasn't the best time to teach someone how to control a skid—but he was simply bulldozing her along with no regard to her feelings.

'You won't. Just do what I did. A bit faster. Now—turn this bend hard.' She did so, feeling the expected skid robbing her of control. Fear jumped in her stomach, but she wobbled the wheel clumsily into the skid—and with sudden pleasure felt the car come under control again. Her stop wasn't quite so graceful, thumping into another drift—but with infinitely less force than before.

'Not bad,' he said drily. 'You might live out the winter. You all right?'

'I'm fine,' she nodded, taking in an uncertain breath.

'It's best to learn these things where and when they happen. That way you won't ever forget the lessons they teach.' Gala nodded, staring fixedly at the wheel. 'Always remember, when you get into a skid, try not to panic. Don't over-correct, and don't be harsh with any of the controls. If you can, get the front wheels in line with the direction the car's going. And you don't have to clutch the wheel, by the way. A light pressure will do.'

'Okay.' She looked at him almost shyly from under her thick lashes. He was wearing jeans that hugged his thighs and a beautifully-designed blue ski-jacket that was, to judge by its airy bulk, filled with featherdown. His boots were of supple, well-worn tan leather. She felt less hostile towards him now than she'd ever done. 'Can I drive you back to the Clinic?' she offered.

'My car's just over there.' He pointed up the road to where a silver-grey sports saloon was parked under the trees. 'I was just going out to the nearest convent.' His eyes glinted irony. 'Thought I'd seduce a few nuns.'

Gala's face reddened. He was so adult, so poised; it was easy for him to make her look a fool. But she knew what she knew, and she wasn't going to be browbeaten by a sarcastic manner. Or an expertise with cars.

'Good luck, Mr Brandon,' she said levelly. He nodded, and climbed out. She watched him walk across the snow to his car, her eyes reflecting the pale glow of the grey sky above. His going seemed to have left the car empty and cold. A big man, with a big personality. Maybe things like stealing someone's wife-to-be just didn't register with Conrad Brandon. He was probably so used to getting his own way that nothing and no-one mattered to him. He climbed into the low-slung car, and drove off without sparing her a glance. Arrogant devil.

Yet her depression was utterly gone. Gala even whistled a few snatches of some pop song as she set off down the road. At least she now knew how to handle a—what was it? A rear-wheel skid. The knowledge sat inside her, cherished like some valuable gift carelessly given.

She was suddenly looking forward to seeing her parents, after all. She turned south at the intersection, and headed for Tunbridge Wells.

She arrived an hour later, just in time for an early tea. The old house was filled with the smell of freshly baked scones, and a fire was burning in the grate. The gleam of copper and polished wood brought back childhood memories as she pushed through the door, shaking off snow.

'Hello, darling. Come in, you must be frozen.' Her mother, vague and elegant as ever, helped her pull off her coat. 'Is that a dent I see on your car?'

'I got into a skid on the way here,' Gala told her, kissing her warm cheek. 'Hit a snowdrift.'

Marcia Fletcher's slightly unfocused eyes widened in alarm. 'Oh no! Gala!'

'Don't fuss, Mum. It was nothing, really. Where's Dad?'

'Reading the Sunday papers. Are you sure you're all right?' She walked Gala through into the drawing-room, where her father was ensconced in his armchair. 'She's crashed her car, Paul.'

'Badly?' Her father struggled his portly frame out of the chair to give her a hug.

'Barely scratched the paint,' Gala assured him. He peered at her over the rims of his spectacles.

'Hmm. Better give it to Sam Colley at the local garage. He'll do a good job. The cold's put some pink in your cheeks, anyhow.' He subsided into his chair, and retreated behind the paper again. 'How's work?' asked his disembodied voice.

'Fine.' She curled up on the sofa, watching her mother wander off back to the kitchen. To some people, her parents would seem impossibly switched-off, but she was secure in their love for her. They just weren't demonstrative people, either of them; but they'd never let her down yet, and she knew they never would.

'Have you read about this aircrash?' he asked. 'Shocking. No regard for procedure at all. It ought never to have happened.' Gala nodded, picking up the colour supplement. When her father had retired from commercial flying, he'd become an air-traffic controller at Heathrow for several years, and he had very firm ideas about air safety. She listened to him muttering on about it with half an ear, warm and contented. She liked being home, liked the air of slight chaos that always prevailed in her parents' home. An inheritance from an uncle had left them quite wealthy, and had enabled them to buy this beautiful old house when Gala had been a fourteen-year-old. Mike had been 23 then, just starting out as a junior pilot with a charter firm, and set to follow in his father's footsteps. Jack, at 17, was still at school. After the gypsy life they'd been living ever since she could remember, the stability and comfort of the Tunbridge Wells house had been like balm to Gala's soul.

Over tea, Gala couldn't help bringing up the subject of Jack's abortive engagement to Crystal Warren. It had been on her mind so much recently, and she'd never really discussed it with her parents. Her mother's face stiffened predictably, though, when the subject was raised.

'I don't think that's a very fit topic to discuss over tea, do you?' she hinted.

'But wasn't it a lucky escape in a way?' Gala pressed. 'I mean, at least it showed us what sort of person Crystal was, didn't it?'

'Exactly what I said at the time,' her father commented, helping himself to cheese.

'Crystal would have made Jack a very nice wife,' Marcia Fletcher sighed. 'If only that *beastly* man hadn't lured her away.'

'Conrad Brandon,' Gala supplied.

'Was that his name?' Her mother made a vague gesture. 'I don't want to talk about it, really. What on earth made you bring it up, Gala? Pass the tea, Paul.'

'Conrad Brandon,' her father nodded, reaching for the teapot. 'You've got a good memory, Gala. He's some kind of a racing champion, evidently. One of these Lotharios with Brilliantined hair, I suppose.'

'Dad! Brilliantine went out *centuries* ago!' She thought of Conrad Brandon's crisp, dark hair for a second, relishing the goodness of a home-baked scone. 'What actually happened, anyway?'

'You remember,' her father said over his teacup. 'You were here. Crystal had been seeing a lot of this chap, and Jack was starting to get annoyed. They were going to be married soon, and I think he felt it was— well, a bit disloyal. We certainly didn't dream that things were going as far as they evidently were with this Brandon man. Anyway, she suddenly pitched up here one night, just a week before the wedding, mark you, and announced that Brandon was taking her off to Barbados. Told us it was all over between her and Jack.'

'She didn't give him back his ring, though,' her mother remembered with tight lips. 'It cost him *hundreds* of pounds.'

'Yes, I'm afraid she was a...' Paul Fletcher thought better of the word he was about to use, 'she was no good, all right,' he amended. 'Jack was well out of that little lot.'

'He was heartbroken,' Marcia said softly. 'I'll never forget his face. Poor Jack. I don't think he's ever got over it. He simply adored her.'

Gala nodded, her head bent over her tea. It didn't seem an appropriate moment to bring up the fact that Conrad Brandon was now one of her patients at the Clinic. Not for long, though. She remembered her resolution to pass him on to Roger Trefusis.

Yes. She'd have to see about that tomorrow.

'And Crystal?' she asked. 'What happened to her in the end?'

'The last I heard of her,' her father said, 'she was modelling in America. But that was ages ago. I wonder what *did* become of her...'

'Well,' Marcia sniffed, 'I hope that awful man didn't spoil her whole life, that's all.'

Gala got up to help clear the table. She thought absently about this afternoon in the snow, the way he'd made her learn how to handle the car. *It's best to learn these things where and when they happen.* A good motto, she reflected later on, staring into the embers of the fire, to carry through life.

Curled up in bed with Pasha that night, listening to the humming of the central heating in her flat, it occurred to her to wonder whether she was really happy.

Of course she was happy! She had everything—a good job, a nice place to live, a loving family.

What about love? whispered the silence. What about people who call you the Ice Princess? Well, love would come, she assured herself. You couldn't expect to find the perfect man while you had a hectic job and no real taste for pubs, clubs and parties. There simply wasn't the time to meet people, and if you didn't mix with people you couldn't expect to find eligible men. But would things ever change? If she was going to work like this for the rest of her life, never meeting anyone except patients, and a few random men who always turned out to be highly unsuitable, she might as well face the fact that she was heading for permanent spinsterhood.

Gala Fletcher? An old spinster? She turned over uneasily, rejecting the thought. Pasha miaowed sleepy disapproval, and climbed back on to her hip. She was reasonably attractive, lively, gifted. How could she possibly end up an old maid? Yet it had happened to a million others. She remembered the librarian at her high school, Miss Lennox, beneath whose spectacles and greying fringe could be seen the faded traces of great beauty. What had happened to Miss Lennox? Some romantic tragedy? Or had life simply passed her by, like an imperceptibly retreating tide, and left her high and dry on the arid beach of a school librarianship?

Depression returned in a wave. She cuddled Pasha to her, wondering what the hell had brought on all these gloomy thoughts. Probably talking about Jack with her parents this afternoon.

Poor Jack. Still, she'd also had her mistake—Brian Matthews. Not that Brian and she had ever planned marriage, the way Crystal and Jack had done. Her mouth turned down in a bitter line. No, any thoughts of marriage had been in her own mind. And it had been Mike, her big brother, who'd finally pointed out the stupidity of her delusions. 'Rich businessmen don't marry penniless students, kid. If you want to stick with Brian, then make sure it's just for the kicks. Because you won't ever be Mrs Matthews, believe me.'

And he'd been right, as always. Brian had announced his engagement that summer, to Laura Deauville, an elegant thirty-year-old heiress with a town house in Paris and a villa on the Cote d'Azur and a block of voting shares in one of the biggest petroleum companies in France.

Brian, with his neat hands and feet, his sharp blue eyes—how wonderful she'd thought him. She'd met him at the Polytechnic where she was training for her physiotherapy diploma. He'd been attending a part-time course on computer management in the evenings, and one winter's night he'd seen her sheltering from the lashing rain in a lecture-theatre doorway, and had offered her a lift. She'd been dazzled by the Rolls, the atmosphere of wealth and sophistication he moved in. A drink in a smart pub that night, and an invitation to a party that weekend had followed. An evening at the theatre, another party, a candlelit dinner, and Gala had felt that she was the only woman in the universe. The fact that he was so young, only in his late twenties, added intriguingly to his allure. He was a *wunderkind*, an ambitious child of the early 80s who'd made a phenomenal success out of an import-export business. When Gala had met him, in her second year, Brian had been riding high on the recession that was closing everyone else down, already learning the art of spending his huge profits. One night he'd taken her to his Highbury flat, shown her the collection of modern art he was building up, fed her three brandies. Even

the electrical grid had come to the support of
seduction that night. There had been a power failure
that had darkened the whole of North London. And
they'd become lovers.

For months he'd been the centre of her life, the
person on whom all her hopes and dreams had been
pinned. She'd just assumed that he was going to
marry her in the end, that she'd spend the rest of
her life with him. Thinking back to her own folly
now brought hot flushes to her cheeks. It was
incredible that she'd never seen that Brian was
going other places. That she was only filling in time
for him while he cast his net after bigger and richer
fish than her.

She'd been just twenty-one when it had ended.
Older, and a lot wiser. Twelve months later she'd
graduated, and had been lucky enough to impress
Lionel Parker and land a probationary year at the
Parker Clinic.

She'd had no more affairs after Brian. Had neither
the time nor the inclination, until now. Maybe Brian
was the reason she'd been letting life slip by her for all
this time. A burned Gala dreading the fire, and all
that. But maybe it was also time she started taking
stock of herself and her prospects!

It occurred to her suddenly that she had promised
to 'phone Richard Schwarzmuller about their dinner-
date this week.

For a moment she thought of putting him off again,
but then made up her mind not to. She couldn't afford
to be so choosy, for Heaven's sake! She glanced at her
watch, then reached for the telephone on her bedside
table.

But she didn't ask Roger to take on Conrad Brandon's
case.

She tried to persuade herself that her reasons were

professional, that she had a responsibility to see it
through to the end; but she was aware—no, *afraid*
might be a better word—of a growing fascination with
the man. Her dislike of him hadn't budged, that was
still there inside her. But she had begun to be
intrigued by Con Brandon despite herself. Intrigued
by the sense of brooding power within him, the
unshakeable will that seemed able to drive him
through any barrier of pain or endurance. He
frightened her, she admitted that readily; but it was
the sort of fear she would feel watching a tiger, or a
wild stallion, or any other thrusting male creature
capable of unleashing awesome force.

They had four sessions in the early part of the week,
continuing the back extension exercises to a more
gruelling level. His recovery was continuing at the
same almost incredible pace. Trying to control him,
though, was like trying to stop a speeding express
train.

'You're going too fast,' she warned him on Tuesday
afternoon as she prepared the machine for half an
hour's traction. 'Injuries like yours take time to heal.
If you push them too hard you could ruin all the
progress you've made over the past week.'

'I don't have all that much time,' he said shortly.
The sheen of sweat made his body gleam like bronze,
and Gala stared with fascination at the droplets that
glittered among the dark hair on his chest and
stomach.

'You're booked until the end of this week,' she
reminded him. 'Lie down, please.' The traction
machine, rather like a sophisticated rack of stainless
steel and leather, was designed to extend the spine,
relieving pressure on damaged discs, and despite its
forbidding appearance, it provided a blessed relief for
patients suffering from the sort of symptoms Con had
had.

'I'm discharging myself this afternoon,' he said casually.

'B-but you can't,' she stammered, taken aback.

'But I am. As soon as this is over.'

'But you aren't fully recovered yet.' She stared at him, her heart sinking unaccountably. 'You need more treatment!'

'I feel as well as I ever will.' His eyes glittered at her sardonically. 'Besides, you were the one so eager to send me away not so long ago. Will you miss me?'

'It's not a question of my missing you,' she snapped. Realising that she'd frozen into immobility, she tightened the strap around his chest and shoulders with fingers that fumbled, and turned her back on him to adjust the machine. 'If you leave now, you'll be back in here within a year, Mr Brandon.'

'I wouldn't count on that.'

'You're too damned confident,' she retorted on a sudden spurt of anger.

'You know as well as I do that I'm perfectly strong,' he challenged. The splendour of his physique was undeniable. For a man with tints of grey at his temples, he had made an astounding recovery.

'I suppose you've got some crazy race lined up?' she asked in disgust.

'I might be racing in the York Moors Rally,' he nodded. 'But I have more important interests to attend to.' Impatience trickled abrasively into his deep voice. 'Come on, Gala—I can't wait all day.'

The voice of someone who wasn't used to being disobeyed, she thought angrily. In a smouldering silence, she adjusted the machine to the right level of tension, and stalked to her desk.

'What interests can you possibly have that are more important than your health?' she demanded after a few minutes' bitter silence.

'I run several businesses,' he replied coolly. 'I

don't want to come back and find the whole lot in chaos.'

'You don't trust your managers, I suppose?'

'I trust human nature to be the same wherever I find it,' he said obliquely. 'Besides, this place bores me stiff.'

'Including me?' The retort was out before she could stop it. From where he lay on the couch she heard his soft laugh, and her cheeks flamed.

'To be frank, Gala, I don't find you terribly interesting, no.'

The amused way he said it made the remark even more crushing, and she found herself really hating him, wishing she had the strength to fight him on his own terms, punish that arrogant strength.

'This place is full of self-pity,' he went on, his eyes closed. His long lashes shaded the harsh lines of his cheeks. 'It smells of hypochondria and boredom and too much money. There are people here who are paying a thousand pounds a week—just to lose weight.'

'So what?' she said fiercely. 'Hypochondriacs and bored millionaires will always come to a place like this. But they're just a minority, and their money goes to very good use, believe me. The Clinic does fantastic work, Mr Brandon. The research going on here is of international importance—and in case you haven't noticed, not all the patients are self-indulgent old women, and not all of them are paying, either!'

'So.' His eyes opened a fraction to give her a slow smile. 'You're proud of your work?'

'Why shouldn't I be?' she demanded. 'You've no right to judge.'

'Touché,' he murmured. 'But I'll still be delighted to see the back of this place.'

'The feeling's mutual,' she assured him sharply.

'There. I knew you secretly approved of my decision to leave.'

'I don't approve at all,' she said in frustration. 'But as far as I'm concerned, you can go to hell your own way, Mr Brandon!'

'You've already chosen yours, I see.'

'What do you mean?'

'Have you ever heard of the whiptail lizard?' he asked. 'It's a very strange creature that lives in Mexico. Apparently, whiptail lizards are capable of unisexual reproduction.' He turned his head to give her that wicked smile. 'The females conceive and give birth without benefit of male intervention. You get whole colonies of females, not a male among them.'

'And what's that supposed to mean?' Gala asked, her eyes as angrily bright as emeralds.

'I shall always think of you as a sort of human whiptail lizard,' he said silkily. 'An interesting curiosity. But completely asexual.'

'*What?*' she gaped.

'I'm not sure what colour whiptail lizards are,' he went on, poker-faced, 'but from now on I shall imagine them as wearing little starched white smocks.' He glanced at her. 'And possessing jade-green eyes.'

'You know how to be cruel,' she gasped. No one had ever dared mock her like that, not *ever*.

'You shouldn't try so hard to be an ice-maiden.' He half-closed his eyes again. 'People are interesting. Whiptail lizards are boring.'

'I'm a professional,' she choked. 'That doesn't mean I'm some kind of robot——'

'A professional.' His tone was razor-edged. 'You think too much about being a professional, Gala. Why not try and be human instead?' He turned his head to study her slim, graceful figure. 'You seem to have the equipment.'

'Don't be ridiculous!' she snapped. 'Of course I'm human!'

'You mean you do have warm blood in your veins?' he queried, raising one dark eyebrow. 'You really have emotions, sexual feelings?'

'Of course I do,' she spat out, her cheeks flaming at the direct question. 'I'm a woman!'

'Really?' His look of surprise was a masterpiece of mockery. 'Well, well. Do I have to stay on this machine all afternoon?'

'You haven't had your full traction yet,' she said, confused by the sudden change of tack.

'I've had plenty,' he assured her drily. He tugged at the straps with lean, strong fingers, and she rose numbly to help him. Whether his mockery had been seriously meant or not, it had shaken her unpleasantly. He stood up, towering over her, and stared down with incredibly intense grey-blue eyes into her own. 'Are you still convinced that I'm the devil's nephew?' he asked, his voice dangerously soft.

'I think you'd better go, Mr Brandon,' she said, cursing her voice for its unsteadiness. 'You must have a lot of packing . . .'

'And you're not going to tell me why.'

'Just leave me alone!' Her nerves were jumping; he was so close that she could smell the maleness of his body, see the velvety texture of his tanned skin.

'Leave you alone? The problem is that you intrigue me.' His fingers traced the line of her cheek more gently, more devastatingly, than she could ever have believed possible. It was as though he had intuitively sensed the yearning that had been there all the time, deep in her heart, had been able to touch it with the tips of his fingers and make it thrill to his command. 'Those green eyes that tilt so mysteriously at the corners. And that soft, soft mouth . . .' As though his touch had turned her into a statue, Gala stood frozen in front of him. With an infinitesimal, secret smile, he reached to the strip of ribbon that secured her ponytail, and pulled it loose. Her hair tumbled around her face in a coppery wave.

'There.' He ran his fingers through the silky stuff, arranging it around her pale cheeks. 'Now you look more like a woman—and less like a physiotherapist.'

'Please go,' she whispered. Her palms were suddenly damp, but her lips were dry as paper. As though she hadn't made a sound, he cupped her face in his hands, and stooped to kiss her. The touch of his mouth was so gentle that she scarcely felt it at first. Her lids fluttered closed, as though she were about to faint, but the broad expanse of his naked chest was against her, supporting her, inviting her to press her breasts against him.

'Kiss me,' he commanded, his breath hot against her lips. She tried dazedly to shake her head, but he wouldn't let her, his fingers running possessively through her hair. 'If you're the woman you say you are—*kiss me*.' The command shattered her will. With the clumsiness of a schoolgirl, she felt her own lips part tremblingly, her face tilting a fraction to meet him. The moist inner part of her lip clung to his for a second, and then she felt herself melting into his arms as they came around her to imprison her body against his. His kiss was ruthless, thrusting, an assault that was meant to dominate and thrill, and Gala yielded to it like dry grass yielding to a field-fire. He possessed her, his arms crushing her as though they were the last, the only people on earth, and his tongue was a shockingly sweet flame that invaded her mouth, taking her captive to his passion.

'No,' she begged, breaking free, 'you m-mustn't, please . . .'

'Mustn't I?' he mocked. Her drugged eyes and bruised mouth were all the answer he needed. He bent to kiss the smooth white column of her neck, his teeth grazing the tender flesh as though he would like to have bitten her there. She shuddered, utterly helpless to stop him. His back was hard and warm under her hands. It was a sweet, treacherous delight to touch the body she'd watched day by day—the male body that was the most beautiful she'd ever seen. 'I may not go, after all,' he murmured, his mouth close to her ear. He inhaled the scent of her hair, almost purring like some great cat. 'You smell sweet, Gala. Like a woman.' He looked down at her, his eyes hooded. 'Would you like me to stay?'

'No!' Like some bird hypnotised by a cobra, she couldn't tear her eyes away from that dark gaze. 'I never want to see you again!'

'Ah, my sweet whiptail lizard.' He unfastened the top button of her smock with sure fingers. 'This garment is so unbecoming. It does nothing for you, my dear. And yet the figure I saw that night at the squash courts wasn't bad at all.' He flicked the opened smock aside, his eyes dropping to the swell of her breasts against the silk blouse she wore underneath. 'Not bad at all.'

'You're arrogant beyond belief,' she said shakily, trying to pull away from him. 'Do you really expect me to just let you do this to me . . .'

'Not at all,' he purred, flicking open the pearl button at the throat of her blouse. 'I rather expect you'll put up a struggle. A brief . . .' His lips brushed her throat. '. . . but delicious struggle.'

Her legs were weak, her heart trembling like a captive bird. He had such power over her that it frightened her; a dark, primitive power that touched her in the deepest recesses of her being. This was nothing to do with the cool, unflustered romance of films and books; this was something that flickered like an arc between his manhood and her womanhood, locking them together in a relationship more intense than anything she'd ever dreamed of.

'Isn't this what you've wanted, right from the first?' he asked in a soft purr.

'No!'

'Yes it is. It's what we've both wanted, ever since we met at the pool that morning.' His fingertips brushed the smooth swell of her breast, making her gasp, wide-eyed. 'Despite all your dislike of me, Gala, despite every prejudice you have against me, you've desired me from the first. Without reason, without shame. As I've desired you.' He kissed her denial into silence, his teeth punishing her lips for the lie. Desire exploded inside her as he cupped her breast in his hand, and she dug her fingers into his naked back, her body arching to meet his. A scalding eternity seemed to pass, and then he was stooping to kiss her throat, the soft hollow of her collarbone, the deep cleft between her full breasts, the concentrated ache of her nipples, until she was whimpering his name, her stomach churning with a desire she'd thought never to feel. He straightened, holding her tight against him with both hands around her hips, and smiled dizzyingly into her eyes.

'You're rather stunning, Gala. Did you know that?' Panting, she held up her mouth shamelessly to be kissed, all pretence of resistance burned out of her now. He obliged—but all too briefly, pulling away as her lips parted to receive his tongue. 'You have a very rare kind of beauty,' he said softly, his eyes caressing her face. 'Sexual, and yet cool as snow. It's fascinating—and maddening.' His smile faded. The smoky eyes became deadly serious. 'Shall I stay?'

Suddenly, the door creaked open, and a head poked round it.

'Am I disturbing? Only I've been waiting ten minutes and I . . .' Mrs Neill broke off, her round eyes saucerlike with astonishment. 'Why, Miss Fletcher! Whatever is going on?'

'Miss Fletcher is giving me a completely new form of physiotherapy,' Con said drily. Anger made his eyes glitter like rapiers. 'You'll have to wait your turn. In the corridor, if you don't mind.' Mrs Neill's outraged face disappeared, and the door banged closed. As though a dream had ended, Gala found herself shivering in his arms, self-hatred flooding her soul. What on earth was she doing? She, who'd been so superior about Crystal Warren, who'd thought she was immune from any attack. Dear God, was she an animal, after all?

'Shall I stay?' Con asked again, his voice urgent.

'No!' She thrust him away from her, her trembling fingers flying to the buttons of her blouse. With this man, of all the men in the world! 'God, haven't you done enough damage?' The colour flared into her white cheeks as she realised how it must have seemed to Mrs Neill. She turned away blindly. 'I hate you! I never want to see you again!'

'So. That's your final word?' Taut and arrogantly male, he spun her round to face him, his eyes now dark with anger.

'Get out,' she hissed, tears pricking hotly behind her eyes, 'before I call Sir Lionel and have you thrown out!'

'That won't be necessary.' Contempt curled his mouth downwards. 'I'm on my way home, have you forgotten?' He flung the red gown around his shoulders and jerked the sash into a knot. 'For a minute back there I thought you really were a woman. I hope you grow up one day. Goodbye, Gala.' He stalked through the door, ignoring a bristling Mrs Neill, and left Gala to give way to the tears that were spilling hot and salty down her cheeks.

CHAPTER FOUR

'MIND the snow.'

Richard Schwarzmuller opened the door of her taxi with Continental gallantry. Gala let him take her arm as with her other hand she hoisted the unaccustomedly long hem of her evening gown over one smooth, silk-clad leg, and clambered out. Richard's brown eyes gleamed approval. The dress, sheer and black, managed to cling to her figure all the way from her breasts down to her calves, and still stay elegant. The slender heels of her black sandals, bought in frantic haste that afternoon to complement her only smart dress, crunched through the crisp snow that was still piled in the streets of London.

'You look absolutely ravishing, Gala!' She smiled at him, aware that his enthusiasm was at least partly genuine; she knew she looked good tonight, especially with her hair braided into a glossy loop, and her mother's pearls at her throat.

'You're not so bad yourself,' she told him. Evening dress suited his dark looks, it was true. He ushered her through the crowded lobby of the Serafina, obviously proud to be seen with her. The way she'd made herself up, not too heavy but distinctly adult, had changed her youthful beauty into something more exotic, and she didn't feel out of place in this very sophisticated hotel. The Serafina Hotel had one of the most fashionable restaurants in London on its towering roof, as well as three separate discotheques in its basement. The rooms were supposed to be stunning, and she recalled Alanna's remark about the seriousness of Richard's intentions. Tonight was going to cost him a bomb—

and if he had set out to impress her, taking her to this place was a very good start.

'You're exceedingly quiet,' he murmured in the elevator. 'Something on your mind?'

'Oh.' She shrugged, trying to be casual. 'I've just been a bit under the weather lately.' Since yesterday morning, to be exact; what had happened between Con and her had disturbed her badly. Ever since then she'd been feeling as though her insides had been turned upside down. She'd had a wretched night, and today hadn't been much better. What he'd said and done had hit her hard in some very vulnerable areas, and she was still reeling. He'd put her through a hoop of emotions that she had scarcely known before, humiliation, anger, confusion, flaring desire.

As for Mrs Neill coming in, right at that moment— she shuddered at the horribleness of it.

'You're shivering.' Concern bringing down his eyebrows, Richard reached for her pulse with a doctor's instinctive fingers. 'Sure you're not getting a cold?'

'I'll be fine.'

'I would have thought the Ice Princess would be immune to cold,' he smiled.

'Don't *you* start,' she groaned. Thrusting the memories of yesterday's passion to the back of her mind, Gala glanced up at the mirrored ceiling of the plush-and-gilt lift. 'This place is fabulous, Richard. Even the lift is palatial.'

'I hope the dinner lives up to expectations,' he smiled. 'I haven't eaten here before, but German friends say the cuisine is excellent. And that's quite a compliment, coming from Berliners.'

'I'm wide-eyed already.' The doors opened, and they walked out on to the thick pile of a cream carpet that looked about an acre wide. 'Wow,' she said, taking in the vast sweep of a floor-to-ceiling window that looked out over the lights of London. The place was impressive on a grand scale, masses of plants separating cool white units containing shops, bars, even telex-rooms—as well as lounge areas where people were already crowding in to sit and talk, and gaze out over the unparalleled view.

'We're early. Shall we have a drink first?' he invited. She nodded gratefully, feeling in need of some stimulation. He took her to one of the cocktail lounges, its soft lights inviting and mellow, and they found a table by the window, with the snowy dome of St Paul's distantly visible in the evening's blue light. Richard ordered her a sherry, a lager for himself.

His clothes sat well on him, she thought; in a few years' time he would be a distinguished-looking man, with that serious air that doctors inevitably seemed to pick up along the way. Yet she didn't feel that spark of attraction towards him that she would have liked. Again, her mind flicked up an image of yesterday, recalling the way she'd shuddered in Con's arms. It had been a shocking experience in a lot of ways. He'd made her almost hate herself for her own physicality. Ruthless and egotistical he might be, but one thing was certain—Con was a man, a real man.

Yet she couldn't imagine anything like that ever happening with Richard Schwarzmuller. Nor had it ever happened with Brian Matthews. Brian had never given her that kind of frightening pleasure, not even when they'd made love. He'd always concentrated on 'putting up a good performance', as he called it, and she'd obliged by trying to seem appreciative; but it hadn't touched her. Not in that way. It was as though she'd discovered sex for the first time yesterday morning. Ice Princess? What a joke.

'I'm sorry,' she apologised, aware that he'd said something. 'I was miles away, Richard. What did you say?'

'I asked you,' he smiled indulgently, 'how your work was going. Any interesting patients?'

'Not really.' Realising this wasn't a very communicative reply, she tried harder. 'Just the usual catalogue of sprains and things. One or two post-operative cases who need careful re-education, but nothing out of the ordinary. And you?'

'I had an interesting case of osteomalacia the other day.' He leaned back reflectively. 'The patient was in considerable pain. Mr Naidu, the tall, very thin Indian. Have you seen him? He'd been passed on to us by his G.P., who hadn't recognised the vitamin D deficiency. It is not exactly common among people of Mr Naidu's social standing.' Richard smiled lightly. 'He owns the Raffles clothing empire. But Mr Naidu has not always been rich. As a child in India, it turns out he suffered from rickets—which, as you know, is the juvenile form of the disease. The deficiency stayed with him, manifested as a malabsorbtion syndrome— am I being too technical for you?'

'Not at all,' Gala said. She didn't really want to talk shop, but she knew from her eighteen months with Brian that men liked nothing better than to talk about their work. 'So you recognised osteomalacia? That was clever of you. It isn't always that easy to diagnose.'

'No.' Richard looked pleased. 'It isn't. But it's something that one associates with people born in third-world countries. Anyway, we've had Mr Naidu on Vitamin D and calcium for a fortnight, and he's already showing a considerable improvement.'

'I'm very pleased.' She drank her sherry, listening to Richard with half an ear. He was obviously a good doctor, concerned about his patients and with the right kind of filing-cabinet mind to make a reliable, thorough diagnostician. He was also clearly trying to make a good impression on her, and she kept nodding and smiling dutifully. The cocktail lounge was filling rapidly, and the buzz of excited conversation was growing louder.

Gala's beauty was also attracting a lot of male glances. A touch of mascara and an eyeshadow that shimmered between ash-grey and green had emphasised the intriguing upward slant of her eyes. Her lips had needed only a touch of gloss to give them an erotic, liquid shine that seemed to invite a clinging kiss. But her skin, cool as alabaster, had needed no cosmetics. There was youth in the slender poise of her neck, a mature beauty in the grace of her movements.

It was nice, she thought suddenly, to be looked at, to receive the flirtatious glances of strange men. It seemed to have been ages since she'd bothered about her appearance or had even been out to someplace as smart as this. Ironically, she was obeying Con Brandon's order—*be a woman*. No doubt he'd be pleased if he could see her now, the bastard! 'Thank you for bringing me here,' she said in a soft voice. 'It's lovely here—and I really am enjoying myself.'

'I'm very glad,' he smiled. 'And the place is lovely.' It was clearly popular, too. Many of the women here wore beautiful clothes, making her own get-up look decidedly plain, and the men had that well-groomed, busy look of people either at the top or heading that way fast. It crossed her mind that she'd love to see one of the rooms in this place, just to glimpse how the other half lived.

'But I'm boring you,' Richard concluded after yet another medical story. His eyes were bright, though, and he probably had no idea that he really *had* been rather dull. He drained his glass. 'Shall we go in and order our dinner?'

'Yes,' she smiled. 'That would be nice.' They rose, and made their way through the crowd towards the restaurant.

'Alanna Cipriani tells me you play squash with her

once a week,' he said. 'You and I must get together for a game sometime.'

'Oh, you'll be much too good for me,' she protested. 'I just play for the exercise . . .' She broke off in shock at the sight of a tall man in immaculate evening dress across the foyer. Think of the Devil! It couldn't be Con Brandon, surely?'

But it was Con, and on his arm was a slim brunette whose exquisite white dress had a spectacularly plunging neckline. Without thinking, Gala tugged at Richard's arm, wanting to avoid any possible contact with Con.

'What is it?' he asked.

'Er—let's look out of the far window,' she suggested hastily, pulling him away. But it was too late. She caught the smoky glint of Con's eyes, and knew he'd seen them. With a sinking heart, she saw Con bend his dark head to say something into his companion's ear, and a second later they were coming over towards Gala and Richard.

'Hello, Gala,' he greeted her pleasantly. The beautiful smile would seem charming to anyone else. The mockery in it was only visible to Gala, and she cursed the scarlet tide she could feel rushing into her face. 'What a pleasant surprise.'

'Good evening, Mr Brandon,' she replied stiffly. Inwardly she was quailing; what horrible embarrassment might he not be planning? It was cursed luck to meet him like this. Con's eyes had shifted to Richard.

'Introduce me to your friend,' he commanded her, the urbane smile still in place. Gala turned unwillingly to Richard.

'Richard, this is a patient . . .' She corrected herself with a touch of acid. 'An *ex*-patient of the Clinic. Con Brandon, Richard Schwarzmuller.'

'Ah.' Con greeted Richard with bluff joviality,

reaching out his hard, bronzed hand. 'You're one of the doctors at the Clinic, aren't you?'

'That is correct,' Richard said with a formal bow. If he was taken aback by Con's arrival, he hid it with European good manners. 'I remember seeing you at the pool once or twice, Mr Brandon. You swim like a champion.'

'And you flatter me,' Con grinned, his teeth white against his tanned skin. He presented the brunette on his arm. 'Gala, meet Coral Bonnington. Coral, this is Gala Fletcher, miracle-worker and expert on the whiptail lizard.' There were two puzzled frowns at this reference, but Gala gritted her teeth and shook the cool hand that was offered her. Coral Bonnington was sensational. That was the only word Gala could find. Tanned even darker than Con, her face was as sweetly oval as a Florentine madonna's. Her slim body was almost fairylike, but the wicked plunge of her neckline between pert, obviously unbrassiered breasts struck a sexy note that would be exciting to any man. Including Richard, it seemed, who was bending over her hand with military diligence. The glittering pendant at her throat, Gala realised, was the letters of her own name picked out in diamonds. Flashy. But stylish. Con Brandon chose his playmates well, she thought viciously.

'I'm delighted to meet you,' Coral Bonnington said in a velvety voice that matched her dark beauty. 'According to Con, you brought him back from the brink of death.'

'Not quite,' Gala said stiffly. She looked for any trace of malice in the other woman's smile, but there seemed to be none, only friendly interest. Not that Gala cared. 'It's been nice seeing you, Mr Brandon,' she went on in a cold voice, 'but Richard and I were just going in for dinner. So if you'll excuse us . . .'

'I most certainly will not,' Con said firmly. From

under black lashes, his eyes travelled appreciatively over her dress, ending on her tightly compressed lips. 'You've fallen into my web, I'm afraid, and there you're going to have to stay.' He glanced into her eyes for a second, then turned to Richard. 'Herr Doctor Schwarzmuller, I'd be very pleased if you and Gala would join us for dinner.'

'But . . .' Gala seethed.

'Not with the rabble in there,' he interrupted. 'In my private rooms. Just the four of us.'

'Your private rooms?' Richard echoed, intrigued.

'We'd much rather dine alone,' Gala said, her tone just short of rudeness. She was cursing Richard for not getting the message. Coral Bonnington's delicate mouth curled into a sweet smile.

'Don't spoil Con's fun, Miss Fletcher. He loves playing the genial host.' She turned her perfect almond eyes on Richard. 'Besides, if you come with us, you'll probably get much better wine than in the restaurant.'

'So?' Richard smiled, looking slightly puzzled. 'Is Mr Brandon a special guest at the Serafina?'

'Mr Brandon *owns* the Serafina,' she corrected with a gentle laugh. Gala turned to Con in astonishment.

'Is that true?' she asked gauchely.

'I'm afraid I do,' Con purred. He watched her reaction through narrowed eyes. 'And Coral is my right-hand woman. Among other things, she runs the discotheques downstairs for me.'

'For you—and for my sins,' Coral smiled. Gala was still stunned by the revelation that Con owned this great hotel. She'd known he was wealthy—but to own a place like this? He must be worth millions. It was impossible to square this kind of power with the savage competition of rally racing. What on earth did he do it for? Coral turned to Con. 'I'd better get down to the discos for ten minutes, Con, and make sure everything's as it should be. I'll join you later.'

'Sure.'

Coral turned to Richard and Gala, excused herself with a smile, and made her way to the lift marked Staff Only. Con reached out and lifted an ivory telephone off its bracket on the wall. 'Louis? There will be four of us for dinner. In my suite, about half an hour, *d'accord*?' He replaced the phone and turned to them. 'I hope I'm not bulldozing you into something you don't want?'

'Not at all,' Richard said pleasantly. Neither of them paid any attention to Gala's furious expression. 'It's extremely kind of you. I had no idea you owned this place, Mr Brandon—but it's one of the best hotels I've ever seen.'

'Please—my name is Conrad, or Con, if you prefer that. Come, let's get out of the mob.' Before Gala could stop him he walked between them, effectively cutting her off from Richard, and took her arm in his. Her brief, venomous struggle was futile. He was far too strong—and anyway, he was already sweeping them through the crowd towards the far end of the room, his other hand on Richard's lean shoulder. Like some benevolent father-figure, she thought acidly. The ruthless side to his nature was smoothly disguised by the mask of geniality he seemed to have put on with his beautiful evening-suit. Except that, if past experience was anything to go by, they were in for an evening of humiliation and mockery. 'I'm glad you like the Serafina,' he was saying, in between dispensing smiles to the dozens of people who seemed to greet him. 'It's only one of the hotels I own, as a matter of fact, but it's my favourite.' He paused to have a quiet word with a member of staff, and then led them up a flight of plushly carpeted stairs and down a wide corridor on the upper level. 'As a mark of which,' he smiled, 'I actually have an apartment here. I use the penthouse as my private suite. It's just through here.'

Gala's first impression of the penthouse was of starkness. A charcoal-grey carpet, black modern furniture silhouetted against walls of deep cream, lighting that glowed from alcoves and recesses. It took a few moments for the sheer beauty of the place to sink in. And the luxury. Nothing in it was superfluous; and every piece of furniture, every painting, every piece of sculpture in its alcove, all had been chosen with the same unerring taste.

Dismissing Richard's compliments with a wave, Con led them through to the sunken conversation-area. Again, without seeming to interfere, he steered Gala to a separate armchair, away from Richard, and she sank into the white wool upholstery with murder in her heart. To make things worse, Richard Schwarzmuller was not disguising the fact that he was deeply impressed by Con and his wealth. 'Marvellous,' he was saying, 'truly marvellous, Conrad.' Why the hell did he have to defer to him? Angrily, Gala wished he'd be more of a man, and stop being fooled by Con's considerable charm.

'You're very silent, Gala,' Con purred, pouring drinks for them. 'I hope nothing's wrong?'

'She's probably a bit over-awed by all this,' Richard said, giving her an irritatingly patronising smile. 'Am I right, Gala?'

'I'm not in the *slightest* over-awed,' Gala said shortly. Richard's eyes widened at her tone, and he stared at her taut expression with obvious incomprehension.

'I'm sorry,' he apologised. 'I didn't mean to offend you.'

'The place was designed to impress,' Con said mildly. 'It gives me an edge when I have to negotiate

with hard-nosed New Yorkers. Ice, Gala?' He brought
her drink over, and leaned forward as he put it into
her hand. 'Stop being such a whiptail,' he murmured,
too low for Richard to hear. His eyes glinted a warning
into hers, and she almost stuck her tongue out at him.
He turned to smile at the German doctor. 'I must
compliment you on your choice of partner, Richard.
Gala may be angry—but she is also very beautiful
tonight.'

'She is indeed,' Richard agreed. He toasted her, his
expression still slightly worried at her obvious anger.
'Cheers.' She didn't respond, disgusted with both of
them. Con's eyes stayed on Gala, assessing her hair, the
sweet curve of her mouth, the alabaster purity of her skin.

'Perhaps her anger makes her beautiful,' he mused.
'In which case we must keep her angry, eh Richard?'
Infuriated by his insistence on forcing his company on
her, after what had happened yesterday, Gala looked
rudely round the room, trying to find something to
insult him with.

'You don't stint yourself,' she remarked caustically.

'Is that an accusation?' He leaned back on a sofa,
casually swirling the ice in his whisky. 'I couldn't help
wondering,' he went on innocently, 'how you got on
with Mrs Neill yesterday.'

'Perfectly well, thank you.' She knew he was
laughing at her behind those damnable eyes, and that
he wasn't fooled by her icy tone. How she had ever
managed to get through the session with Mrs Neill,
her eyes red from weeping and her hair still in
disorder, was a complete mystery to her. Her brain
must have switched over to autopilot.

'Is that a Kandinsky?' Richard asked, staring at an
abstract canvas on one wall. When Con nodded, he got
up and walked over to it with an expression of
disbelief. 'It's magnificent! How on earth did you
acquire this?'

'I bought it at auction. Sotheby's.'

'I've never seen a finer example,' Richard breathed, 'outside a museum.'

'Really?' Con looked pleased. 'That earns you a double, Herr Doctor.' He poured the generous measure into Richard's glass, and added ice with silver tongs. Despite herself, Gala stared across at the painting. It shimmered with an extraordinary light, vivid scarlet and yellow patterns against a turquoise background. It was a lovely thing, and for a second her anger left her. She rose to examine it more closely. There was a silence for a minute or so as she and Richard stared at the canvas.

'That one won't be long out of a museum,' Con said. 'I'm donating it to the Birmingham Art Gallery. I want it to be seen.' Gala looked across at him to find his eyes on her face, as though assessing her reaction once again.

'Very generous,' she said drily. 'King Conrad sharing his wealth with the peasants.'

Unexpectedly, he grinned, perfect teeth glinting white in a heartstopping smile. 'There's no quarter with you, is there, Gala?'

'I don't know what you're talking about,' she replied dourly.

Richard glanced from one to the other, stroking his moustache with nervous fingers. 'Excuse me for asking this,' he ventured, 'but is there perhaps some quarrel between you?'

'If you haven't worked that out by now,' she said unkindly, turning away from the painting and going back to the conversation-area, 'you're not as observant a doctor as you ought to be.' With a mutinous glint in her green eyes, Gala sat down on the sofa, and patted the cushion beside her, her eyes uttering a silent command to Richard Schwarzmuller. For once he got the message, and came to sit beside her. She thrust her hand through the crook of his elbow, and clasped her fingers possessively on his forearm. 'That's better,' she said meaningfully. She wanted to show Con that she didn't give a damn for his wealth or his sex-appeal. Richard, looking both surprised and delighted, patted her hand.

Still smiling, Con walked slowly down the steps to them, one hand in his pocket. He was undeniably dazzling in the formal clothes. The severely-cut jacket hugged the power of his shoulders, the snowy white of his shirt emphasising the deep, even tan of his skin.

'Human relationships are funny things,' he said, his deep voice smooth as the seventeen-year-old malt he'd given them. 'They get off on the wrong foot, sometimes for quite the wrong reasons, and then they become very difficult to steer back on course again.' Grey-blue eyes met hers with a jolt. 'No matter how perfect they ought to have been.'

'Perhaps it isn't worth trying to steer them back on course, as you put it,' Richard suggested.

'Perhaps,' Con nodded indifferently. Had she hurt him? Gala looked steadfastly down into her drink, suddenly feeling she'd been worse than a whiptail lizard tonight. She'd been a bitch.

The pause was interrupted by the entry of Coral Bonnington, cool and lovely in her white gown.

'Please don't get up,' she insisted as Richard began to rise. Her eyes flicked to Gala's hands round his arm, and Gala had the sudden feeling that Coral would be able to guess a great deal of what had been happening in her absence from minor signs like that. Coral Bonnington was a lot more than a pretty face. 'It's turning out a lively night downstairs,' she informed them, helping herself to a drink at the sideboard with easy familiarity. 'Do you dance? Perhaps you'd like to take a look in after dinner.'

'That would be fun,' Richard said eagerly. Gala's

acid glance was wasted on him—he'd obviously already forgotten that there was any ill-feeling between her and Con. Coral was enough to make him forget everything, she realised. He started telling her about discos he'd been to as a medical student in Bonn. With the same easy familiarity, Coral moved to Con's side, and slid one slender brown hand around his arm as she listened. The gesture was graceful, a perfect compromise between possession and affection. Gala felt an unreasoning resentment twist her heart. Was this beautiful creature Con's lover as well as his employee? It didn't help her to know in her heart that Coral's gesture had probably been in response to her own contact with Richard. Whatever else she was, Coral Bonnington was loyal to Con. Loyal as steel.

The conversation broadened out, only Gala taking little or no part in it. Con was a fascinating talker, and Coral made a beautiful hostess, matching his formidable charm with her own delicate grace. In a sudden vision, Gala saw them as lovers. They were a perfect match. The stab of jealousy in her was so painful that she dug her nails into Richard's arm, making him yelp in surprise. Jealousy?

Yes, she told herself fiercely. Jealousy. Just because you had a reason to hate Conrad Brandon didn't mean you had to deny that he was a magnificent male creature. Any woman would feel the same about him. Especially with someone like Coral to compete with. But even with a partner like Coral Bonnington obviously doting on him, Con still had to make casual passes at other women. Like herself. Crystal Warren had probably been as casual a fling as that.

Half an hour later, one of the waiters knocked at the door to announce that their meal had been brought through from the kitchen. Dinner was served in the surprisingly small dining-room that adjoined the chamber they were in. The window, left undraped,

commanded a breathtaking view of Lincoln's Inn and
the Gray's Inn Gardens beyond. In the snow, it was a
fairytale picture, and Gala realised that the room had
been made small to keep the sense of intimacy that
might be lost by this panoramic view.

The meal was unexpectedly simple, too, but the
ingredients—a traditional roast with perfectly cooked
fresh vegetables—were impeccable. It was what she
would have chosen herself, and Gala guessed that
Coral Bonnington had been in charge of the dinner.
The claret, as Coral had promised, was a noble vintage
that went to Gala's head much too quickly, helping to
melt the inner ball of anger that she'd been so
carefully trying to nurture. Over dinner, her frosty
manner thawed helplessly. The candlelight helped to
create an atmosphere of magic, and by the time Coral
was pouring fragrant Turkish coffee, Gala was
gurgling with laughter at Con's stories.

They didn't bother to leave the table after the
waiters had cleared. A close, happy atmosphere had
settled around them, almost burying the tension that
they all knew existed between Gala and Con. The
brandy that Con insisted they try with their coffee was
redolent of ancient summers. Gala felt its insidious
fire creeping along her veins, reminding her disturb-
ingly of what had happened yesterday.

'It's *grappa*,' Con informed her, his eyes on her
mouth as she tasted the clear yet burning liquid. 'A
friend of mine gets it for me in the hills of
Lombardia, northern Italy.' The candlelight was
ambiguous as it flickered across his face. Sometimes
it showed the urbane mask of the man-of-the-world
he so obviously was; at others, when the shadows
drifted around his eyes and under his cheekbones,
Gala caught the pagan savagery she knew lurked just
beneath that veneer.

'Richard and I are very lucky men tonight,' he went

on in his purring voice. 'We must have two of the most beautiful women in London at our table.' He caught Gala's sardonically raised eyebrow and smiled, cat-like. 'Both beautiful—and yet such different types. Coral has the dark mystery of the Mediterranean in her face. But she is deceptive. Her gentleness hides sharp claws. Gala, on the other hand, with her flaming hair and emerald eyes, lives up to the redhead tradition. All claws and spitting fury. And yet I think Gala's sharp claws hide gentleness.'

'You mustn't judge us like that,' Coral smiled. 'You'll have the Women's Movement down on your neck. Besides, it's we, rather than you, who are lucky.'

'Oh, I do so agree,' Gala put in, letting just enough poison drip into her voice to let Con know she wasn't going to be taken in by any old hokum he might dream up.

But whether it was the alcohol, or just the sense of *bien-etre* induced by the delicious meal, she felt that old fascination with Con Brandon igniting inside her again.

'Tell me,' she said, during a lull in the conversation a little later, 'what makes you drive in rallies?'

'Because they're there,' he smiled.

'That won't do,' she protested, leaning forward. 'You're always dodging the question. All right— you've been British champion twice running, and I can imagine there's a certain thrill to what you do. But it's dangerous, and there's always the chance that you'll be killed or badly injured. There are scars all over you from crashes you've had.' Twin candle-flames flickered green in her eyes. 'Why, then? You've got all this. You could live happily ever after in this— this empire of yours. Why don't you retire from racing?'

'Perhaps I will,' he shrugged. 'When I've found it.'

'Found what?' Gala wanted to know.

'Found the missing factor. The factor that I replace with rallying.'

'Missing factor?' Richard said with a laugh. 'What could possibly be missing from your life?'

'You're medical people. You tell me.' But his eyes were on Gala's alone, and she felt the skin on her stomach contract at the expression in them.

'Besides,' Coral smiled, 'you must give the others a chance.' She cradled her glass in both hands, turning to Richard and Gala. 'The scars aren't from rallying, by the way. Con's too good to crash. Except deliberately.'

'Deliberately?' Richard echoed.

'I used to be a test-driver for a big German car manufacturer,' Con said casually. 'A crash-test driver.'

'You're joking,' Gala said in disbelief.

'I'm not. Crash-tests are vital in determining how cars are designed. Crumple zones, safety cells, anti-roll bars, seatbelts—everything of that sort is designed and refined through crash-testing.'

'But I thought they used dummies,' Richard said, putting down his glass.

'Not always.' Con smiled at their faces. 'It was almost fun in a way. They used to wire me up with sensors and transmitters, packing a whole lot of monitoring equipment behind the front seat. And then I used to drive into walls at high speed, or flip the car, or get into collisions with heavy goods lorries . . .'

'Stop.' Gala covered her ears, shuddering. Coral Bonnington glanced at her, then drained her glass, her eyes shaded by long lashes. 'For God's sake,' Gala went on in a numb voice, 'what possessed you to take on a job like that?'

'The pay was fantastic,' he said lightly. 'And I was poor. I wanted the money to buy Riverside Lodge, an old house on the Thames which was falling into rack and ruin. I succeeded.' Gala recalled Alanna's mention of a 'lovely ramshackle old cottage by the river' that Con had been living in when she'd met him.

'The one you sold for a hundred thousand?' she asked with a hint of malice.

'Has a little bird been talking to you?' Con replied mildly, but didn't confirm or deny it.

'You're lucky to be alive,' Richard suggested, looking at Con with a lot more awe than Gala liked. 'Didn't you ever get hurt?'

'Occasionally. It didn't seem to matter so much then. I was a lot younger and wilder. I'd been drifting ever since my parents died, and I felt I didn't have too much to live for. Except racing. You don't get paid much as a rally driver—not until you win something big—and testing was a good way to make money.'

'So you bought your house,' Gala prompted. 'What then?'

'Home-ownership settled me a little,' he smiled, draining his glass. 'Especially as I had to work day and night on Riverside Lodge, repairing the neglect and damage of centuries. The roof had to be completely replaced, just for one thing. Finding eighteenth-century tiles is not exactly an easy task. Then the foundations had to be shored up—I did that with a friend who knew about concrete. After that came repanelling, plastering—you name it, I did it. It wasn't like driving. It came hard at first.'

'I'll bet.' Alanna hadn't mentioned all that side of it. As a seventeen-year-old, she thought ironically, Alanna wouldn't have noticed all the hard work that went on behind the glamorous James Dean image. 'So you sold it for a healthy profit?'

'It was a wrench,' he admitted, 'but financially healthy, yes. With the money I bought Stratos Motors, which wasn't all that different a proposition from Riverside Lodge, actually. Stratos were a once-prestigious West End firm who'd fallen on bad times during the recession. It was run by these two amazing old Edwardian gentlemen who still arrived for work in top-hats. No idea how to run a modern business, of course, but Mr Barker and Mr Budworthy had plenty of style. Unfortunately, they also had more debts than motors, and the car-buying public were avoiding them like the plague. But with the arrogance of youth, I thought I could make it work. More *grappa*? Come on, Richard, you're not drinking nearly enough of it.' He poured for all of them. 'I must be boring you stiff.'

'It passes the time,' Gala said, hiding her very real absorption with the story. 'How old were you?'

'Twenty-five.'

'And Stratos Motors?' she asked. '*Did* you make it work?'

'I know Stratos Motors,' Richard said unexpectedly. 'It's got a plate-glass front about a mile wide, and it's packed with Rolls-Royces and Maseratis, all gleaming under the spotlights.'

'I was lucky enough to get a Rolls franchise,' Con nodded. 'And I made a speciality of importing foreign exotics for the more-money-than-brains brigade. It's amazing how many people still have the money to spend sixty thousand on a brand-new Lamborghini. For the more serious-minded I stocked Porsches, Lotuses, good second-hand performance cars of all kinds. And Stratos Motors did start working, yes.'

'That sounds like the understatement of the year,' Gala said quietly. 'Stratos, the Serafina—what else do you own, Con?'

'A few more hotels. A few shares. A garage full of classic cars. A house or two.' His eyes glinted. 'Not much else. What do you own, Gala?'

'A very old, very small first-floor flat. And a cat. Oh, and an orange Morris.'

'Which you drive execrably,' he concluded for her.

'I'm not that bad,' she said defensively. 'I got half-way through a pilot's licence, you know.'

'Really?'

'Yes, really,' she told him. 'My Dad was teaching me when I was sixteen. I was a brilliant navigator.

'But you gave up,' he suggested.

'I got airsick,' she confessed, flushing. 'I always do in small planes.'

'I trust other forms of motion don't have the same effect.' The smoky expression in his eyes suddenly made her heart flop inside her like a hooked fish. 'Shall we dance?'

CHAPTER FIVE

THE jumping, blazing lights were hypnotic, exploding in time to the music, that crashed out of the massive speakers around the dance-floor. It felt like years since she'd danced so energetically—or had so much fun. She couldn't see Richard or Coral for the crowd, and in any case, Con was keeping her much too busy. He moved with style, much more style than she herself had, and he seemed utterly tireless. There was no let-up in the music, either, and she had to beg for a rest when at last she felt she had not an ounce of breath left. He led her, panting to their table on the balcony, out of range of the biggest speakers. Everyone here seemed to have the stamina of athletes, and she followed Con's pointing finger to where Richard and Coral were still spinning in the midst of the floor. The drinks Con had pressed on him had obviously inspired him to dervish-like activity.

'Your weekly game of squash apparently isn't enough,' he smiled, passing her her drink. 'The good Herr Doctor seems to be enjoying himself.'

'I'd forgotten what a test of endurance discos were,' she panted, and gulped at the refreshing liquid. 'Gosh, aren't there some good dancers? Did you see that tall black girl?'

'She's a professional.' Apparently unfazed, he offered her his handkerchief to mop her flushed face with. 'She dances with one of the best small companies in London. She's here two or three times a week. See that boy with the long hair, over there? He's a dancer, too. You often see him on television.'

'Oh, *yes*!' Gala recognised the taut little body and

pug face. 'This must be the in-place if people like that come here.' She looked round. The place had been designed using brightly-painted tubular steel and high-technology fittings, giving a vivid, urgent feel. The balcony they were on was raised a few feet above the dance-floor, the tables arranged round sculpted aluminium units. The noise, even up here, was fierce. 'It's very exciting!'

'For kids, really.' Con grinned wryly. 'The other two discos are a bit less frenetic, but I wanted you to see this one. I'm about twenty years too old for this place.'

'Nonsense.' She shot him a quick look. 'Every girl in the place is staring at you in fascination. But I know what you mean. I'm going to ache tomorrow!'

'That's my motto. Dance today, ache tomorrow.'

'Did Coral design this place?' she asked him.

'She designed all three. You wouldn't think it to look at her, but under that cool exterior lies the soul of a raver.'

'Indeed,' Gala said drily. He smiled at her, amused lines bracketing his mouth.

'You sound jealous.'

'Rubbish!'

'No?' He mocked her with an eyebrow.

'No.' She drank, lowering her eyelashes. 'So tell me about Coral.'

'Ah. Well, when I bought the Serafina a few years ago, it was very old-fashioned, and becoming a bit shabby. Elegant, but staid, if you can imagine that. It had marvellous views, though, and an excellent substructure to build on.'

'Like Stratos,' she suggested, watching his face.

'Like Stratos,' he acknowledged. 'Like Riverside Lodge. If you have a successful formula, you should stick to it.'

'And yours was finding the potential in shabby old places?'

'You could say that.'

'Brilliant,' she conceded. 'But a rather nerve-racking gamble, surely?'

Again, a glint of amusement softened the penetrating eyes. 'Who do you want to hear about—me or Coral?'

'Coral,' she said after an inward struggle. She was longing to know whether Coral was his lover, whether she was going to share his bed tonight, but though she knew he probably had read her unspoken questions, she didn't dare ask them.

'Well,' he went on, leaning back, 'I wanted to keep parts of the hotel in their pre-war elegance, but I also had to brighten parts of it up to attract younger people. I wanted to see the place bright and gay, full of happy people. Discos and restaurants were the obvious answer. That's where Coral came in.' He drained his glass, and she watched the muscular ripple of his throat. 'I advertised for someone to take charge of the discos, and among the hundreds of people who applied for the job was this extraordinary punk. Green and pink hair, clothes like something left over after a nuclear explosion, make-up straight out of The Munsters . . .'

'*Coral?*' Gala asked incredulously.

'None other.' He slipped off his jacket and tie, folded them over an empty chair, and unfastened the collar of his silk shirt. Suddenly he was no longer an aristocratic *bon viveur*, but a supple-waisted toreador, radiating a dangerous male sex-appeal. The crisp curls at his throat reminded her sharply of the dark hair that covered his chest and stomach, and Gala suddenly had to lick her dry lips to moisten them.

'That's hard to believe,' she stammered, trying to find her way back into the conversation. 'I mean— Coral could pose for *Vogue* right now.'

'My influence,' he said smugly. He reached for her hand, and opened her clenched fingers, ignoring her alarmed expression. 'I'm noted for having a good influence on women,' he said silkily.

'Like Alanna Cipriani,' she suggested. 'You've obviously enslaved *her*.' He drew a finger thoughtfully down her palm, making her skin crawl with nervous pleasure.

'Alanna's a nice kid.' He laced his fingers through hers, trapping her hand between his. 'But let's stick to Coral for the time being. You could see talent simply oozing out of her. And underneath the horrible get-up you could also see real beauty. So I offered her the job—on condition that she altered her image completely. I said I refused to work with someone who looked like Cruella De Ville on a bad day. So I took charge of Coral's image for a while.' He looked back at the dance-floor thoughtfully. 'Good clothes, good salons, proper make-up. It took weeks for her hair to look anything like normal, but there was a practically overnight transformation in all other departments.'

'I'll bet,' Gala said acidly. The Pygmalion story aroused her worst feelings of jealousy. 'Just how far did your—influence—extend?'

'Now you're being impertinent,' he grinned, showing perfect white teeth in an all-too-rare smile. His smiles were beautiful, she thought, they seemed to light up the whole room—but there weren't enough of them. If only she knew how to unlock them more often! 'Anyway,' he concluded, 'Coral's been with us for three years now, and I wouldn't part with her for thousands.'

'Oh.' The monosyllable sounded so dismal that he laughed softly, and lifted her wrist to his lips, kissing the sensitive pulse gently. The music slid into a slow number for the first time in an hour, and the flashing lights subsided into a soft blue glow.

'Come on.' He rose, pulling her to her feet. 'This tempo oughtn't to tax you too much.'

Unwillingly, she had to follow. It was a shock, though, to be taken firmly in his arms, and to feel his lean, muscular body close against hers.

'Hey!'

'Don't be silly,' he reproved, easily resisting her efforts to move away. 'This is only dancing.'

'Is it?' Her heart was pounding, and not from the exertion either. 'I haven't forgotten yesterday.'

'Neither have I,' he purred in quite a different tone. Gala flushed, her hands still braced against his hard chest.

'I don't trust you one inch, Con Brandon,' she told him.

'I can't exactly rape you on the dance-floor, Gala.' But she was too aware of his thighs brushing against hers to be much reassured. His body was hard against the pit of her stomach, his hands caressing her back with the gentleness of a master horseman controlling a nervous mare. 'For God's sake, relax!'

'I don't *want* to relax.' But she tried hard to unstiffen her body, which seemed to have gone into a generalised spasm at his touch. He drew her close against him, his lips brushing her cheek in a way that made goosebumps shiver down her spine.

'That's better,' she felt, rather than heard, him say. The warm breath against her ear was deliciously, alarmingly, reminiscent of yesterday. 'What's that perfume you're wearing?'

'Nahema,' she told him in a wavering voice.

'It's not bad. But I like the smell of your skin better.'

'I didn't know it had a smell,' she said with a nervous laugh.

'Oh yes.' He caressed the silken smoothness of her shoulders with possessive enjoyment. 'When you got close to me, during physiotherapy at the Clinic, I could smell it. Feminine and distracting, and very,

very sexy.' The music shifted into a leisurely blues number, and his body urged hers into the primitive rhythm with long, slow thrusts that seemed to melt all her resolutions like ice in the sun. 'I found it rather hard to concentrate on the exercises.'

'Which reminds me,' Gala said huskily, 'I don't think you ought to be dancing with a back like yours.'

'You'd be surprised at the things I can do with a back like mine,' he said in a sensuous growl.

'That's just crude,' she snapped, looking up at him with a frown, and meeting a wicked expression. 'God, you know how to upset me! I never know when you're serious and when you're teasing!'

'You talk as though you had a right to know.' His hips surged hard, sexy, against her own. 'Besides, I am crude. I'm also selfish and egotistical, and the devil is my uncle. Or had you forgotten? So what are you doing with me?'

'You kidnapped me,' she retorted. 'Or have *you* forgotten?'

'Call it a hijack,' he corrected, grey eyes watching her through thick lashes. 'I simply borrowed you from the good doctor for an hour or two.'

'Where *is* Richard?' she asked, nervously craning her neck to see through the crowd. 'He's been gone for ages.'

'Don't worry about him,' he said, iron-hard arms preventing her from squirming away. 'They've gone to sit down now.' She followed his gaze to the balcony, where Richard was indeed sitting, apparently in deep conversation with Coral Bonnington. 'Coral seems to be keeping him busy,' he remarked casually.

'Was that your idea?' Gala demanded, her upward-slanting eyes narrowing in sudden suspicion.

'Oh come on!' Irritation gave his voice a perilous edge, and she quailed. 'You don't have to fight me a hundred per cent of the time, damn it!'

'But——'

'I'm trying to get you to shed that skin of yours, whiptail! Don't fight me the *whole* way.'

'I'm happy the way I am,' she snapped nervously.

'That beautiful mouth requires discipline.' His lips were harsh against hers, his kiss a mixture of punishment and pleasure. Involuntarily, her eyes closed, shutting out the world as that familiar ache of desire jolted into life inside her. Her whimper went unheard against the smooth music. His kiss was what she yearned for, yet she knew it was wrong, the worst kind of folly to let it go on. But the touch of his tongue was unbearably erotic, caressing her mouth in a deliberate echo of the act of love. Gala felt herself sliding into the maelstrom, exactly as his cruelly expert lovemaking intended her to. Her slender arms crept around his neck, pulling him closer, begging him to deepen the kiss, touch her even more tenderly. Their bodies seemed to fuse, their skins sliding together with the shocking intimacy of lovers.

She managed to break free, shuddering. 'People will see,' she whispered jumpily.

'Who?' he demanded, holding her close. 'Dear Richard?'

'Yes!'

'Come off it. You don't give a damn about Richard, and you know it.'

'You take a lot for granted,' she hissed, wishing she had the strength to pull away from him.

'Do you know what they call you at the Clinic?' he asked.

'Yes,' she said in a low voice. 'It isn't very funny.'

'So show them it isn't true,' he invited.

'Why? It *is* true!' But touching him seemed to satisfy some profound need in her, and the contact was too thrilling, too precious, to lose now. He kissed her again, his lips warm on her eyelids. The struggle to keep him at bay was emotionally exhausting; she felt herself dissolve against him, her mouth caressing his naked throat. She wanted to be lost in him, lost in the smell of his skin, the warm strength of his body, to be utterly obliterated in the consummation she knew he wanted. His desire was arrogant against her, shameless.

As the song ended, giving way to a more up-tempo number, Gala grasped the last of her moral courage and pushed herself out of his arms, and raised trembling hands to push her tumbled hair out of her eyes. Her cherished plait was threatening to disintegrate into streaming chaos.

'I—I don't want to dance any more, Con. Can we do something else? Please.'

He watched her, one fist on his hip. 'Such as?' he asked.

'Anything.' She groped in her fuddled mind for an idea. 'Richard and I were dying to see the rest of the hotel. Couldn't you sh-show us some of the rooms?'

'I don't think Richard's very interested in seeing any rooms right now,' he commented drily.

'Oh no, I'm s-sure he'd love to,' she said anxiously. Anything to get off this dance-floor, and away from the intoxication of Con's touch!

'Very well,' he shrugged indifferently. 'If you really want, I'll take you up to see one of the suites with pleasure. Wait here, I'll go up and call them.' She nodded, and leaned back weakly, trying to arrange her hair as she watched his tall figure moving through the tables up to the balcony. He reached the table where Richard and Coral were in close confabulation, and spoke to them for a few minutes. Then Richard waved cheerfully to where Gala was standing, and Con started down back alone, his dinner-jacket slung over his shoulder.

'Aren't they coming?' she demanded as he reached her.

'They want to dance some more,' Con told her. 'Richard says he's seen plenty of hotel rooms. So I've said we'll go up alone and see them back here in a few minutes.'

'Oh,' Gala said, suddenly not too pleased with her own idea. 'As long as we aren't too long.' She waved rather half-heartedly to Richard and Coral, who both waved back, and let Con lead her away.

Her legs were horribly weak as they pushed through the noisy crowd to the exit, and into the silent peace of the elevator.

'I'll get Reception to check which suites are empty. I wouldn't want to burst in on one of my guests. You're looking a bit pale,' he went on gently, touching her cheek.

'It's n-nothing.' She looked away from the piercing grey beauty of his eyes. 'It was just a bit—a bit hot in there.'

'It certainly was,' he agreed mildly, the mockery in his tone too far below the surface for her to protest.

'The Lakeland suite is vacant, Mr Brandon,' the efficient beauty at Reception informed them. 'Shall I get Tickford to have it open for you?'

'No thanks. I'll take the keys up myself.' With her arm firmly held under his, Con led Gala back to the lift and pressed the button for the fifth floor.

'I've never stayed in a place like this in my whole life,' she told him. 'I suppose it's very expensive?'

'Hideously,' he agreed calmly. 'But worth it, as I hope you're going to agree.'

Gala smiled up at him uncertainly. He was so handsome, so authoritative. He seemed to dominate any company effortlessly, not through bombast, but simply because he was so clearly a man who didn't need to prove a single thing. Men, as she'd seen with

Richard, automatically deferred to him. Perhaps it was some ancient pack-respect for the dominant male. As for women, Gala doubted whether even the coldest would be able to withstand that purposeful, formidable will of his.

A phrase of Alanna's crept into her mind. *Con represented everything that was delicious—and forbidden.* Yes, that quality in him was easy to see now. What woman, within range of those fjord-deep eyes and that husky voice, could suppress a trembling in her heart?

When Con pushed open the impressive door that read *The Lakeland Suite*, Gala let out a little gasp. The rooms beyond were magnificent, furnished in a symphony of blues and greys. The tone was set by a massive autumnal painting of Lake Coniston that hung over the Adam-style fireplace, and picked up in the shimmering blue drapes at each arched window, the grey silk coverings on the Empire furniture, the misty carpeting. Even the slender marble pillars that separated the rooms were a deep green that echoed Lakeland stone. Considerable style and taste had been brought to this suite, and as she walked in fascination through to the next rooms, she realised that much of the furniture was genuinely antique, some of it very beautiful.

'Are all the suites like this?' she breathed, peeping into a marbled bathroom with sunken onyx bath and its own jacuzzi.

'Some of them are,' he nodded. He was watching her reactions, as he'd done before. But if he took pleasure in her admiration, his rugged face gave nothing away.

'What on *earth* did it cost you to set this place up?' she gasped. He leaned against an archway, smiling slightly.

'Think of a figure, then double it. A lot. But people

love this suite, and that makes them prepared to pay the tariff.'

'I don't even want to know what it is,' she said, shaking her burnished head in wonderment. The suite had everything, including luxurious dressing-gowns in the cupboards and a selection of track-suits that Con told her were for the use of people who wanted to jog in one of the nearby parks. You could walk into this suite with nothing more than a few changes of clothes, and be perfectly contented for weeks. She walked through to the bedroom. The bed was modern, but the sky-blue canopy that swept down over it gave it the elegantly intimate feeling of an Elizabethan four-poster. The bedroom furniture was unusually delicate and beautiful, and four large, fine modern paintings of lake scenes gave the room a free feeling for all its grace. 'It's absolutely heavenly.' She sat down almost reverently on the bed, feeling the mattress yield deliciously beneath her weight. 'Mmm. Paradise! What sort of people sleep here? Princes and maharanis?'

'Not usually,' he said, amused. 'Just people prepared to pay for their comforts. Not always such rich people, either.' He watched her with brooding eyes, his smile fading. Her slender figure in its sheath of black silk was disarmingly small against the vast blue quilt. 'Would you like to sleep here?'

'I'd love to,' she said with a little laugh. 'You talk as though it was possible!'

He strolled towards her, slinging his jacket over the back of a chair. 'Why not?'

'Why not?' she echoed. Her laugh was less confident now. 'Well, for one thing, it might upset Richard Schwarzmuller. He's supposed to be taking me home.'

'Ah.' He sat down beside her, secret amusement glinting somewhere in his eyes. 'I must confess to perpetrating a minor deception on your behalf. The good doctor is under the impression that you're home already.'

'How . . .?' she stammered.

'I told him that you weren't feeling very well. The noise and heat had apparently given you a headache. He and Coral seemed to be having a good time, and when I volunteered to drive you home myself, he seemed quite pleased.'

'Did he now!' Her face paling with anger, Gala jumped to her feet. 'God, you're the most high-handed man I've ever met, Con—and as for Richard bloody Schwarzmuller, he must be simple-minded to believe a tale like that!'

'He *did* have a lot of claret at dinner,' Con said, his expression unrepentant. 'Perhaps he's not thinking too straight.' He leaned back on the bed, a lean, sexy figure, and gave her an unabashedly wicked grin. 'Don't look so amazed. All's fair.'

'Do you mean to tell me,' Gala quavered in outrage, 'that you deliberately set out to get Richard sozzled— why, you monster, you planned this from the second you saw us in the foyer!'

'I wanted you all to myself,' he replied calmly. 'I needed to talk to you.'

'What about?' Gala demanded, trying to control her breathing, which had quickened unpleasantly.

'Firstly, I wanted to apologise for yesterday.' The expression on that passionate mouth didn't look very apologetic, though. 'I was extremely rude to you, which I shouldn't have been. And then I—well when I touched you, I lost control a little.'

'It seemed to me you were in perfect control the whole time,' she said acidly. 'Is that all?'

'No.' He stood and reached out unexpectedly to touch her face, his eyes becoming cloudy with a desire she recognised all too well. 'I wanted to talk about us, Gala.'

'There's nothing to say,' she stammered, her heart pounding.

'Maybe not with words. But with our bodies . . .' He smiled gently. 'There's much to say. And you know it.'

'How dare you,' she whispered, but even in her own ears it sounded half-hearted. 'You mean you've brought me up here . . .'

'To make love to you. Yes.'

'So.' Trying desperately to find calm among her whirling emotions, Gala turned away from him. 'You intend to add rape to your other accomplishments, then?'

His laugh was soft, genuinely amused. 'My melodramatic Gala. Do you think I'd lay a finger on you—if I didn't know you wanted me as much as I want you?'

'That's a lie,' she shot back, turning to him in outrage. 'I don't want you in the slightest.'

'But your voice falters when you say that,' he pointed out.

'Because you frighten me!'

'I'm the big bad wolf, and you're Little Red Riding-Hood. But you wouldn't have come up here with me if you hadn't known, in your heart, that I wanted to make love to you.' His smile was utterly certain of her. So certain that she had to drop her eyes, feeling her cheeks flush deep red.

'Is sex the be-all and end-all, then?' she asked thickly. 'I'm not the sort of woman who jumps from bed to bed, Con.'

'You don't have to tell me that,' he answered gently. 'I know it.'

'Then you must know that I couldn't give my body to anyone I couldn't love. And believe me, Con, I could never in a million years love you.'

'A million years is a long time.' He made her feel

about twelve years old when he talked to her like that.
And her pulses were throbbing dizzily at his nearness.
Fear and desire—two emotions that ought to be
frantically contradictory, yet which were adding up to
a wildly intoxicating cocktail in her veins. 'Your skin
is so beautiful,' he whispered, trailing his fingers over
her naked shoulders. 'I love to touch you, Gala. Can
you deny that you love it, too?'

'No,' she whispered. God, if only this was right, if
only he were anyone except Conrad Brandon! He drew
her closer, his lips brushing her temple as he drew the
zip at the back of her dress slowly down. His caress
became a track of fire against her body. His fingertips
trailed lightly up the silken skin of her spine, to the
fine hair at the back of her neck, releasing her braid
and pulling the long, auburn hair loose from its
disciplined pattern.

She tried to pull away from him, but his mouth had
already found hers, his tongue parting her lips,
pushing through her teeth, opening her as though to
make her realise how much she really ached for his
love. She pulled him against her in a deep pang of
longing, her hands running hungrily through his crisp
hair. With a deep, murmured endearment, he sank
down on to the bed, pulling her with him, easing the
black silk dress off her shoulders, his hands caressing
the smooth curve of her hips and drawing her to him.

'This is all wrong,' she moaned. The flood in her
was bursting its banks, but she couldn't shake off the
guilt and worry that nagged at her mind.

'It's the only right thing in a very wrong world,' he
murmured. 'I've wanted you from the moment I saw
you, Gala.'

'But I *can't* . . .' The hair of his chest crackled
against her fingers, his man's nipples dark and hard
under her restless palms. His mouth found hers,
kissing her protests into silence, caressing her eyelids,

tugging at her earlobes with sharp teeth. Gala had no strength to resist as he pushed her back against the yielding mattress. It was a sweet torment to feel the honed strength of his loins thrusting against her, only the veil of her clothes keeping them from consummating a passion that had begun to burn like a furnace.

'Is Richard your lover?' he demanded huskily, smoky eyes burning into her own.

'You've got no business to ask,' she panted.

'*Is he?*' He reinforced the growl with steel fingers that bit into her arms.

'Of course not,' she whispered, her drugged eyelids closing and a faint smile touching her clinging lips.

'Good,' he said, his voice a purr of sheer, feline pleasure as he looked down at her. 'That saves me having to fight a duel with him.'

Gala laughed almost painfully. 'The thought of you fighting a duel with anyone! You're the most dishonourable man I've ever known!'

'Is that so?' His eyes narrowed in mock-anger, Con hauled his shirt off in one movement. 'Assassinating him, then.'

'That's more your style.' Her breath coming shallow and fast, Gala couldn't stop her hands from reaching out to touch his body—the magnificent male body she'd been forced to watch and touch so often before. God, she wanted him! If there was any ice in her, it had long ago been scorched into steam. 'I'm not going to let you make love to me, Con,' she said, as though the words alone might make it come true. 'I'm not. I'm not.'

'Of course not. You only came here to look at the suite.' But his fingers were already peeling her silk slip away, exposing the cool white curve of her breasts.

'My sweet Gala,' he whispered, hooded eyes taking in the tight pink buds of her aroused nipples, 'you're so beautiful.'

'Please don't do this to me . . .' Her voice had never had much authority when it came to giving orders to Con Brandon, but now it was little more than a warm breath whose soft tones contradicted the words she so desperately wanted to find. He caressed the satin of her upward-tilting breasts with gentle fingers, then with hungering lips, making her tremble helplessly. And when he held her tight, the naked contact of their bodies was like the fulfilment of a dream. It had never been like this with Brian, not even remotely like this. Brian's lovemaking had been a routine, uninspired exercise of bodies. This was a heart-racing drug that rushed in her veins and made every inch of her silky skin intensely, painfully, *alive*. His mind, as much as his body, seemed to be making love to her, as though this were a thing of souls, not only of the physical world.

His body was hot against hers, the brush of her nipples against the hair on his chest a nerve-twisting pleasure. Her voice was half a groan as she broke free of his drowning kiss, digging her nails into the hard power of his shoulders.

'Don't, please!'

'For God's sake!' He shook his head, frustration puckering his eyes. 'What *is* it with you, Gala? I know you want this as much as I do—so what makes you hold back all the time?'

'I *don't* want this, Con.' She arched her neck as he cupped her breasts, the possession of his hands exquisite against their aching fullness.

'Your body tells me you're lying,' he said, his thumbs moving in a heart-stoppingly slow caress to and fro across her nipples. 'And you're not a virgin. I knew that at once by the way your body moved against mine. You've known a man's love before—why are you trying to deny mine? Gala, I promise you this will be different from anything else you've ever known!'

'D'you think I don't know that!' Tormented, Gala twisted out of his arms, and lay face-down on to the counterpane, the hot ache of her breasts flattened against the cool silk. This intoxicatingly sweet dream had to stop, now, before it was too late. Con wasn't the man her heart ached for him to be. He was a force that could easily destroy her, and she *had* to try and escape that fatal attraction, no matter how much it hurt. 'Can't you just accept that this is something I mustn't do?'

'Gala . . .' His fingers brushed through her tumbled autumn hair. 'I don't understand you, girl.' He cradled her in his arms, his chest warm against her back, and touched her shoulder with his lips. 'The smell of you is enough to drive me crazy. We could have so much together, more than you could ever imagine.'

'No,' she choked.

'*No*, always *no*.' She felt his wry smile as he laid his head against her back. 'Do you know any other words?'

'Please,' she begged, 'let me go home now. I'll call a cab . . .'

'Damn you!' His arms tightened round her threateningly. 'Do you have any idea what you're doing to me?'

'You started this! I begged you not to!' Nevertheless, she was nestling against him, somehow knowing instinctively that she was safe.

'You wouldn't by any chance be playing hard to get?' His husky question was followed by a warm kiss against the tender skin of her neck.

'I swear I'm not,' she whispered. 'Oh, Con, we shouldn't even be together!'

'Why on earth not? You talk as though you belonged to some exclusive religious sect.' She shivered as she felt his lips caress the downy skin of her back, tracing the curved line of her spine. 'You're lovely,' he said possessively. 'I bet you don't have prolapsed intervertebral discs.'

'*Please* don't . . .' He rolled her over suddenly, and she tried to cross her arms to cover her naked breasts, but he wouldn't let her. His expression was amused—but also frustrated.

'Why, Gala?' His eyes dropped to her taut nipples, his mouth hungry. 'Look how you need me! And yet you persist in saying no!'

'There's a difference between men and women,' she whispered. 'Sex isn't everything with us—as it seems to be with you.'

'Not everything.' She closed her eyes helplessly as he kissed the sensitive peaks, one after another. 'But a lot, I admit. I'm not going to force my attentions on you, Gala. Not after what happened last time. But I'm not letting you up until you swear you'll see me again.'

'No,' she said firmly, shaking her head. 'That's impossible.'

'Is it?' This time his teeth grazed her skin, a pleasure-pain that it was impossible not to cry out against. 'Then perhaps I'll change my mind, after all . . .'

'You're cruel,' she shuddered. 'Don't, please . . .'

'I need to see you, Gala. Just as you need to see me.'

'You're wasting your time—I've already got a lover,' she said desperately.

'Liar.' His mouth was caressing her midriff now, moving lower, down the smooth plane of her stomach. 'Spend Sunday with me.'

'No!' She arched as his tongue probed her navel, and ran her fingers shakily through his hair. His kisses were perilously sweet, inflaming her, taking her a long way beyond the limit of her will-power. 'Yes, *yes*. If you'll promise it's the last time!'

'I'll promise anything.' He was so handsome when

he smiled. The laughter-lines transformed his face, seeming to warm her whole world. 'You don't know how close you came to the valley of the shadow.'

'I do,' she said significantly, 'believe me.' Part of her wanted to laugh with him, be happy and free in their mutual desire and pleasure; but her mind was shrilling like a jammed alarm-bell. This was all wrong. How many women had he seduced with exactly these charms, this animal sex-appeal? She started pulling her clothes on hastily, guiltily.

'You're like a convent-girl having her first tumble,' he smiled. 'Will you have to rush home and say a hundred Hail Marys?'

'A thousand wouldn't help,' she muttered, struggling with her zipper.

'Here, let me help.' He tugged the zip up for her.

'I mean it,' she said, turning to face him. 'I'll see you Sunday, but it'll be the last time ever. I *mean* it!'

'If you say so,' he said calmly. But the glint in those narrowed eyes told her he was taking about as much notice as an express-train would of a rabbit in its path. For a moment it was on the tip of her tongue to confront him with what she knew about him and Crystal. But that would be to bring this wonderful dream to a halt. Not yet, her heart pleaded, not yet. In despair she got up and tried to pull the tangled glory of her hair into some kind of order. She felt his eyes on her. 'I'll call that cab now,' she said, embarrassed at the intimacy of letting him see her dress like this.

'You don't have to get a cab.' He stood up, and started pulling his shirt and jacket on. 'I'll drive you home.' She watched in the mirror as he walked to the cabinet to pour himself a massive whisky while she dressed. Her whole body seemed numb as she fumbled to straighten her dress.

'You've got to drive,' she reminded him as he gulped the amber liquid down as though it were water.

'I also have to put out a fire,' he said drily, and she flushed. In the mirror her face was beautiful now, lit with a kind of inner radiance. Was that what a few kisses did? Or was this the face of a woman falling in love? Rejecting both thoughts, she turned to him. I'm ready now.'

'You're a lot quicker going out than you were coming in,' he observed. 'Do I really scare you that much?'

'It's not a question of being scared,' she replied. 'Just of using everyday common sense. Like the young lady of Niger.'

'Who rode with a smile on a tiger?'

'Exactly,' she nodded. 'If you recall, they returned from the ride with the lady inside . . .'

'And the smile on the face of the tiger. Except that there are no tigers on the banks of the Niger, Gala.'

'I may have my metaphors mixed,' Gala said meaningfully, 'but the underlying point is still the same.'

'What's happened to the good old values,' he asked, grinning, 'like trust?'

His car was parked in a special bay in the cavernous underground parking-garage beneath the Serafina. The black leather interior smelled of luxury and speed, and she sat dreamily folded in her wrap as he guided the sleek silver-grey coupé out into the snowy streets. 'Is this the car you rally in?' she asked.

'A special version of this one.'

'Is it fast?'

'Frighteningly so.' He switched on the cassette-player, filling the interior with smooth jazz. 'But not in the middle of London, in the snow.'

'What are we going to do on Sunday?' she asked him.

'Have a civilised lunch together. Talk. Perhaps I'll show you my car collection. Nothing too depraved.'

'Hmm.' She didn't speak again except to give him directions, but as he pulled up in her street, between the shabby gentility of the Georgian terrace and the featureless modernity of the council development, he turned to her gravely.

'Thank you for a delightful evening, Gala. I don't suppose you're going to offer me a night-cap?'

'Once in the lion's mouth is enough,' she said. But there was real pleasure in the kiss she gave him. It was blissful to pretend they were two ordinary people, going through the ordinary, miraculous process of falling in love. It was like a dream she could wrap herself in, shutting out the rest of the universe. 'Thank you,' she whispered.

'I'll pick you up here. Ten o'clock on Sunday morning.'

She slipped out and leaned through the window to stare into his eyes. One last time, she told herself. One more blissful day with him, and then over. For good.

'Good night, Con.'

'Be good.' The red tail-lights disappeared down the empty, snow-lined street. One more time, she told herself, as though it were some charm that might save her from giving her heart to him.

One more time.

But before she even reached her front door, her eyes were wet.

CHAPTER SIX

THE next day, rain arrived in long gusts that lashed remorselessly at the trees and the Clinic windows. In the streets the snow turned to slush, and by evening was almost gone. The countryside emerged from its romantic blanket of white, looking, Gala thought dully as she drove homewards, as though it were unpleasantly surprised to find itself so drab and grey. As she reached London, the leaden clouds lifted for an unenthusiastic sunset, and the winter's twilight fell smoky and long-shadowed over the city.

Con's face had haunted her all day long. The excitement of last night had worn off, leaving her with a sickening sense of the impossibility of their relationship. But this feeling she had for him wasn't like anything she'd ever known. It wasn't simple. It was a mixture of opposites that conflicted wildly—attraction, repulsion, desire, distrust. And it just wouldn't leave her alone, as though it were something that had grown into her being, spreading roots into the farthest recesses of her emotions. Tearing herself away from him last night had been like trying to wrench off a part of herself. And the thought of seeing him again the day after tomorrow made her whole being thrill, as though he alone could bring sunshine to her world.

In a few short weeks, he'd managed to affect her in a way that went farther inside than any relationship she'd ever had before. Brian had been exciting, yes—but not because of what he was. She'd been, she now realised, more than half in love with love itself. In her way, she'd used Brian just as much as he'd used her. He'd been a substitute for something else, something she'd only just now discovered with Con. There had been no real sorrow in her parting with Brian, and that spoke volumes for the kind of relationship they'd had.

It was going to take a great deal, she now realised, to get over Con Brandon. What she was going through with him was something vivid, unique, unforgettable.

She'd passed a rather depressing day's work. She'd been worrying about Con, trying to sort out the rights and wrongs of it, trying to tell herself that he wasn't to be trusted, that he'd betrayed others, perhaps countless times. Totally uninspired, she'd just gone through the motions with her patients. At lunchtime she'd actually walked away from Richard Schwarzmuller while he'd still been talking. His jovial, 'Some night, eh?' had been calculated to infuriate her. And she didn't want to hear what had happened between him and Coral, either. If Richard imagined she was going to forgive his thoughtlessness that easily, he had another think coming. Not that she had the energy to even keep angry at Richard for more than a few minutes. All she seemed to want to do was curl up and sleep, so that she didn't have to think until Sunday. When she'd see *him* again.

That was what addiction meant.

She got home, fed Pasha, and flopped into a sofa. The sound of the doorbell made her groan, but she heaved herself up and opened it.

The man standing outside was in his late twenties, looking very smart in a new charcoal suit she hadn't seen on him before. He had close-cropped hair of the same auburn shade as her own, and the same somehow vulnerable green eyes.

'Hi, sis.'

'*Jack!*' She gave her brother a quick hug, and led him inside. 'You look marvellous in that suit! Business must be looking up.'

'I've had some good commissions lately,' he acknowledged. Where Mike's voice was deep and masculine, like their father's, Jack's was a light, pleasant tenor. The lack of warmth in it, however, was noticeable.

'You sound done in! Come and sit down. Just knocked off?'

'At five,' he nodded. His face was still boyish at twenty-seven, but Gala couldn't help noticing worry-lines around his eyes. Success always had its price, she reflected.

'Have you had something to eat yet?'

'I'm not very hungry,' Jack said, dropping his briefcase next to the armchair. 'Gala, I came to talk to you.'

'Well, have a cup of coffee, at least.'

'I don't want coffee.' Pasha hopped comfortably into his lap, only to be unceremoniously ejected. 'Sit down, Gala, don't fuss.'

'I wouldn't mind some coffee myself,' she said plaintively. 'What is it, Jacky? Something wrong?'

'Yes, something's wrong,' he said shortly.

'Well, tell me,' Gala invited, slightly worried. She came to perch on the arm of his chair, and looked at him with affectionate eyes. 'What is it?'

'Have you been going out with Conrad Brandon?' The sharp question made her blink. Then she felt her face stiffen.

'Who told you that?'

'Is it true?' he demanded, a slight flush of anger on his cheekbones.

The situation made her wince. 'No. It's not true, Jack.' How could she possibly explain the complicated things that had been happening? Her brother's bony face expressed incredulity.

'You mean you weren't dancing with him at the Serafina last night? You didn't let him kiss you on the middle of the dance floor? You didn't go up to his room and spend the night with him?'

'*No*,' Gala said fiercely. 'That's a lie!'

'Two of my friends saw you.' The temper that went with Jack's red hair was clenching his jaw now. 'Either you're lying or they are.'

'Wait a minute.' Sighing, Gala slipped into the seat next to him. 'Yes, I was with Con last night . . .'

'"Con"?' he echoed.

'Conrad Brandon,' she amended, flushing in her turn. 'But I didn't go there with him. I went to the Serafina with a friend from work, a doctor called Richard Schwarzmuller. Con happens to own the hotel, and he just wanted to dance with me——'

Jack interrupted with a snort of disgust. 'You mean he dances with everyone who comes to his hotel? Come off it, Galatea!'

'Let me explain.' The disbelief in his eyes hurt her. It was a damnable situation, and ironic beyond belief that Jack should be berating *her* for being with Con! And yet she did have something to hide, a lot to hide. It was horrible to have to deceive Jack, but he'd never understand. No man would ever understand. She went on, picking her words carefully. 'Of course I'd met him before. He arrived at the Clinic as a patient last month. I was assigned to give him physiotherapy for compressed cervical discs . . .'

'You had to treat him?'

'I had no choice, Jack.'

'How long has this been going on?' Jack demanded, his eyes shocked. 'Weeks?'

'Nothing's been going on,' she said shortly. 'Con was a patient of mine for a few weeks, yes. But there was nothing between us. How could there be, after what he did to you? And then we met at the hotel last night. He muscled in between me and Richard, insisted on dancing with me.' She dropped her eyes.

'And on the dance-floor, he *did* kiss me, yes. But it was against my will, I assure you.'

'I don't believe you!' His voice vibrated as though it were about to break. 'Tom and Anthea said you were behaving like lovers. Embracing, shamelessly, in front of everyone. They couldn't believe it at first. All my friends know what that bastard did to me.' He gulped helplessly, eyes bitterly hurt. 'Gala, how *could* you?'

'Oh, Jack!' Cursing Tom and Anthea Smith for their spying eyes, Gala tried to find a way of explaining the impossible to her brother. 'It isn't the way you think at all! I've been as cold as I possibly could to him.' The memory of last night rose up in her mind, and she fought it down. She had to lie, if for no other reason than to spare Jack's feelings. 'I wouldn't even speak to him, hardly. But I just couldn't stop him from kissing me. For God's sake, I didn't want it! But he's twenty times stronger than I am . . .'

'You went up to his room,' Jack accused her. 'They saw you go, hand in hand.'

'They must have done little else last night except watch me,' Gala said drily. 'I didn't go to *his* room, Jacky. He took me up to show me one of the suites. I just wanted to see what they were like . . .'

'I thought you were hardly speaking to him!' he interrupted.

'I just wanted to get off the dance-floor . . .'

'To go into a room—alone—with *him*?'

'Oh, damn. This just isn't coming out right.' Gala tugged at her silky hair in frustration. 'Jack, you must believe me—what Tom and Anthea think they saw last night was nothing. Nothing at all. Yes, Con was making a pass at me. But he didn't know who I was, he still doesn't. Jack, for heaven's sake stop looking so betrayed!'

'Gala, I just can't believe all this.' Jack stood up, and walked jerkily to the window. 'Your private life is

your private life, and I've never interfered, not once.
But with *that* man, of all the people in the world—how
could you do it?'

'Jack!' Gala lifted her eyes and strangled a scream
between clenched teeth. To be torn between Jack and
Con was intolerable. 'There's nothing between me and
Con! Do I have to swear it on the Bible?'

'You keep calling him "Con",' Jack shot back,
spinning round accusingly.

'That's his name,' she said in frustration. 'Conrad,
Con, Conrad Brandon, whatever you like. He's not
some Mr X. I can't call him "that man" all the time.'

Jack's eyes didn't leave hers. 'Are you sleeping with
him?'

'You don't have any damn right to ask me that,'
Gala flared up, her temper igniting like hot petrol at
last. 'I wouldn't tell you if I was!'

'Oh, Gala.' Suddenly his face puckered, almost as it
used to do when he cried as a boy. 'Have you no
loyalty? Or if you haven't, haven't you even got any
taste? To go kissing a man like that in the most public
of places—what are you trying to do?'

'I'm not trying to do anything.' She lay back with
an explosive sigh, trying to keep her temper under
control. If Con were here now, she could easily have
brained him for bringing all this down on her. If Jack
were ever to find out she'd agreed to spend Sunday
with Con, he'd go crazy. 'Jack, you simply aren't
listening to me. I'm not Con Brandon's lover. Not.
His. Lover. I hardly *know* him. If you choose to
believe your friends before me, then go ahead. But I'm
telling you here and now that you've got the whole
story cockeyed.'

Jack turned his back on her, staring out at the dingy
sunset with unseeing eyes. 'You're not in love with
him, then?'

The question lashed on the raw, and made her

flinch again. She opened her mouth to deny it, but no sound would come out. Was she in love with him? Heaven only knew. Would 'love' explain this miserable feeling inside? Her almost helpless attraction towards a man she had every reason to distrust and hate? If she was, it couldn't possibly be anything more than an infatuation——

'Are you?' He turned to meet her darkened eyes. 'Gala, I'm worried about you. And Mom and Dad are desperate.'

She sat up, her whirling thoughts disrupted. 'Oh, no! You haven't told them?'

'I had to.'

'Oh, you ninny!'

'I called them today, and we all agreed that I should come and see you tonight and talk it over. Gala, if you take up with Brandon, they'll never speak to you again, you realise that?'

'For Pete's sake! I'm not taking up with anybody, let alone Con. I loathe him! I hate the very ground he walks on, Jack.'

'And yet you were hugging and kissing him last night in the smartest disco in London.' He came back to sit facing her, his pale face earnest. 'Okay, I can accept that what Brandon did to *me* might not mean all that much to you. You were only a kid at the time. But you must see what kind of man he is. He'll only hurt you, worse than you could ever imagine.'

That was what she'd been telling herself all day. It was reassuring to have Jack reinforce her own opinion. 'I know that! I haven't the slightest intention of going anywhere or doing anything with Conrad Brandon. Can't you get that into your red head? What did you have to go and tell Mom and Dad for! You've given them all the wrong ideas!'

'Dad told me how you'd been asking all sorts of questions about Brandon a fortnight ago. Now we know why. You were getting involved with him even then. Listen,' he said urgently, hushing her protests, 'he's bad news, Gala. He lives fast and hard, and the women in his life mean less than nothing. They're just there to be used and discarded. You've got to keep away from him——'

'That's exactly what I've been trying to do,' she interrupted, 'for weeks now!'

'You mean he's persecuting you?'

'Not exactly.' Gala groped for the words. 'He doesn't even know who I am.'

'Well why haven't you told him?'

Because I couldn't bear to lose him. But she couldn't tell Jack that. She could only tell him the other part of the truth. 'I never told him while he was at the Clinic because he was a patient, and I was trying to keep a professional distance from him. And last night—well, maybe I should have told him. That might have put him off surer than anything. But he'd given us dinner, and——'

'You had dinner with him?' Jack gaped.

'I told you,' she said impatiently. 'He hijacked me and Richard. Hell, if you don't believe me, ask Richard yourself! I'll give you his number!'

'Oh, sis, I don't want to pry into your life.' Jack shut his eyes, looking as tired as she felt. 'What has or hasn't happened between you and Brandon is your own business, you're right.' He met her eyes, looking older than his age suddenly. 'Mom and Dad and I just want to stop you from being hurt, Gala. We only want one thing. Your promise that you won't ever see him again.'

Somehow she managed to turn her guilty start into a smile. 'That's easy to give. I haven't the remotest intention of seeing him again!' That was a cold lie, but she told herself it was a white one. After all, when she saw Con again, it would be to tell him it was all over. And that was a *certainty*.

'You mean that?'

'Of course I do.' She shuffled the lies away, hating herself for her pragmatism. 'As for what your precious friends saw last night, Con simply grabbed me and kissed me. In case you don't know, he's about seven feet tall. I didn't have a chance of resisting. Can't you give me the benefit of the doubt?'

'You're my sister,' Jack said, the ghost of a smile breaking through his solemnity. 'I can give you anything.'

'Jacky.' She reached out to ruffle his hair. Older than her he might be, but she'd always somehow felt responsible for him. There was something childlike about him beneath the talent and the adult brain. 'After what he did to you and Crystal, did you really think I could fall for Con Brandon? Believe me, Jack, all the interest was on his side. And when someone eventually tells him I'm your sister, I don't expect he'll come within a mile of me.'

'I wouldn't bet on that,' Jack said grimly. 'From all accounts he's a wilful man, and if he's got an interest in you he's bound to take some shaking off. But we'll be there to help you. And if he insists on pestering you, we'll call in the police.'

'All you need is a pair of mutton-chop whiskers to make you the perfect Victorian father,' Gala said, with a hint of irony in her gentle face. 'I promise you I'll never see Con again, if I can help it. And you can tell Mom and Dad that. Okay?'

'Okay.' His angular face now lit by a smile, Jack reached out for her hand. 'I'm so glad you've seen sense, Gala. With your obstinate constitution, I expected quite a battle on my hands.'

Gala returned his smile. But she wasn't feeling quite so cheerful inside. She'd given a convincing performance, even down to the injured innocence. But would that be enough to convince her own unruly heart?

She'd left a very large part of herself with Con, and there was no way to go about getting it back. Sunday was going to be a watershed. Even if she herself hadn't wanted to end whatever had started with Con, Jack had laid it on the line for her—it was Con or them. She gave her brother's hand a squeeze, praying that she'd meant what she'd just said, and that dreams of Con weren't going to haunt her tonight.

'Well,' she said, trying to sound brisk, 'so *that's* over. Shall we have something to eat now?'

'I've got a better idea.' Jack reached into his pocket and waved a bulging wallet. 'Get your glad rags on— I'm taking you to a celebration dinner.'

'Okay.' Feeling utterly unworthy, Gala went to change. Guilt was an unexpectedly heavy burden. When she saw Con on Sunday, she promised her mirror, it would definitely, incontrovertably, *unquestionably* be the last time.

She was still repeating that to herself as she got out of Con's car on Sunday morning and followed him through a high pair of wrought-iron gates.

'I thought you lived at the Serafina,' she said as they walked up the stone stairway, ducking to avoid the trailing jasmine that was beginning to bud as if in defiance of the cold weather.

'I stay there now and then. But I couldn't live there. As an environment it's far too artificial.' The doorway to the old Victorian house was framed in ivy. The whole place, grey stone and mullioned windows, seemed to Gala utterly at odds with what she knew of Con's character. It was beautiful, gentle, almost quaint. The gardens were large and full of mature trees, and the house was practically invisible from the road. In the distance, the great glass hoops of the Temperate Plant House were visible, emerging from the greenery of Kew Gardens. Con opened the door and turned to her. 'This place is a lot more congenial. Especially for Sundays.'

Feeling slightly strange, Gala walked into the hall. Antiques, oil-paintings, Persian rugs. An atmosphere of neo-Classical tranquillity. A long way from the uncompromising modernity of the black-and-white suite at the Serafina. The impression of wealth and taste was definitely there, but not nearly so aggressively manifested.

'It's beautiful,' she gasped in surprise.

There was an ironic glint in his eyes as he took her coat. 'You sound as though you didn't expect it to be.'

'I didn't expect it to be so—tasteful.' The distant clink of crockery caught her ear. She turned to Con. 'Is someone else here?'

'Mrs Belling. My housekeeper.' He smiled at her. 'If you sniff the air, you'll notice that even as we speak she's making our lunch. You'll meet her later on. Come through.'

The drawing-room was both elegant and comfortable, gleaming with the fine wood of eighteenth- and nineteenth-century furniture and centred around an exquisite Turkish rug in muted reds and greens. The only familiar note came with the Expressionist painting of a speeding car on one wall. Con poured her the sherry she asked for, sank into an armchair and turned deep grey eyes on her.

'You keep staring at me,' he said mildly. 'Anything wrong?'

'You're just different today,' Gala said in confusion. While she herself had worn a smart linen suit, Con was in faded jeans that clung to his hips and thighs and a leather jacket that was supple with years of use. It wasn't that the clothes didn't suit him; if anything, they made him look sexier and more masculine than ever. But they suggested a man rather different from the thrusting, polished man of affairs she'd been used to.

'I'm not always a capitalist monster,' he said, as though reading her thoughts. 'You're old enough to know by now, my love, that what most people show to the world is only a mask.'

'The trouble starts,' Gala sighed, going to the window and looking out at the row of lichen-softened statues in the garden, 'when you try to find out how far the mask goes, and where the real person begins.'

'And where does the real Gala Fletcher begin?' He watched her over the rim of his glass. 'You've got a mask, too. A neat, starched uniform and a neat, starched expression.'

She had to giggle. 'Am I that bad?'

'You're starting to improve. I told you I'd be good for you. But I have to admit you're a good physiotherapist. I haven't had the slightest trouble since you treated me.'

'Until you go and wreck yourself in some other way,' she said drily. She paused in front of a beautiful landscape in oils. 'You were really worried about your back, weren't you?'

'I have to admit that the prospect of life in a wheelchair was looming in my nightmares,' he nodded.

'You should give up rally-driving,' she said decisively, sitting down at last.

'And do what?' he probed.

'Marry.' For some reason the word made her flush, but she went on regardless. 'I'm sure at least one of the hundreds of girls you have in tow must be eligible.'

'What makes you think I've got hundreds of girls in tow?' he enquired.

'Well, you're——' She stopped short, embarrassed. 'You know what you are, Con. You're intriguing, for one thing. I know practically nothing about you, except that your parents died when you were young and that you used to be a test-driver. I don't even know where you were born.'

'I was born at Le Mans,' he said, poker-faced.

'Well, that's a good start to a racing career,' Gala smiled, not sure whether he was teasing her or not.

'It's true.' He got up, lithe and tall, and pulled a leather-bound photograph album out of a bookshelf. 'Come and sit on the sofa with me.' She obeyed, inquisitive, and curled up beside him, looking over his broad shoulder. He opened the album to a monochrome photograph of a man in overalls, helmet and goggles standing next to a racing-car, against a background of cheering spectators. The fashions were from about twenty years ago. 'That's my father, next to the Porsche he won the fifty-two hour endurance race in.'

'"Christopher Brandon",' Gala read from the banner draped over the car. The handsome face was like Con's, and there was the same air of devil-may-care gallantry about the pose.

'They still talk about him in racing circles,' Con said gently. 'He was real class, my dad. Won a lot of races—and made a lot of friends, which is more. This is my mother.' The woman looking over her shoulder into the camera was dark, beautiful, her smile both provocative and sad. Her scarf was fluttering in the breeze, and the background, again, was a racing-circuit. 'Her name was Eden,' he told Gala. 'She was even prettier than that. She'd modelled for Balmain before she married my father.' His eyes, normally as direct and piercing as a bird of prey's, were as soft as mist now. Gala sat silently cradling her drink, feeling the warm tautness of his body next to hers. 'That's me.' His lean finger rested on a shot of a small boy sitting on the mean-looking bonnet of a racing-car.

'Aged about ten.' Bare knees and tousled hair, but that dazzling grin was unmistakably Con. There were several other shots from the same period, the three of them on beaches, sprawling on lawns, in the rooms of various houses—but mostly next to cars or on race-tracks. Almost all had some connection with motor racing in them; many were simply of banks of cars, blurred with speed or dimmed with dust. Now and then, Christopher Brandon appeared, with the laurel-wreath of victory round his neck. 'That was my childhood, Gala. One racing circuit after another. My father was a pro, you see. One of the best. He had a real passion for racing, something in his blood. My mother and I just followed where my dad went. Where the races took him.'

'Were you the only child?'

'Yes. I think they were planning more, but they never got around to it. There probably wasn't time. We lived like gypsies, always in hotels or caravans somewhere in Europe.'

Gala studied a colour picture of the strikingly handsome family grouped around a scarlet E-type Jaguar. 'You all look very happy,' she murmured.

'We were. Blissfully happy. It was an exciting life, whatever else it was. Exciting and always on the move. That's how I came to be born at Le Mans. My Dad came third that year. Like you, though, my mother always wanted my father to give up racing.' He smiled sadly. 'That was something else they never got around to, I guess.'

She glanced at his aquiline profile. 'Were they— killed in a crash?'

'My father never crashed a car in his life. No, they drowned.' In silence he went through the pages of the album, and found a yellowing clipping from some newspaper. Gala took it, recognising Con's parents in the photograph. The headline read RACING STAR

DROWNS TRYING TO RESCUE WIFE. 'Oh no,' she whispered. There seemed nothing to say. She read through the story. Eden Brandon had been washed out by the current one summer's day on a Cornish beach. Her husband had plunged in after her. Neither had returned from the water alive. There was a list of the races Christopher Brandon had won, and a mention of their surviving son. 'Seventeen,' Gala said quietly. 'Where were you?'

'At a boarding-school by then, cramming for a university place.' He turned the pages to a class-photograph, and then put his arm around her, pulling her close by his side. The stunningly handsome young man in the front row was Con. Gala looked at the level eyes, the mature mouth. 'You must have been heartbroken.'

'At first,' he nodded. He looked up, his eyes meeting hers with that familiar tingle of electricity. 'Then I went into a murderous rage.'

'Against who?'

'Everything, my sweet Gala.' He smiled a little tightly. 'I never got to university. I joined the Army instead, but couldn't stomach the regimentation. Also, I kept going AWOL to race in rallies, and that didn't endear me to my commanding officer. In desperation they made me a despatch-rider. That was fun, until some officer clocked me doing a hundred and twenty down a country road one day.' His expression was wicked. 'After two years I resigned.'

'What then?'

He leaned back, folding the book in his lap. 'Then? Oh, two dozen jobs in two dozen different countries. Packer, fisherman, labourer, mechanic, you name it.'

'A misspent youth altogether,' Gala said, trying to sound disapproving. But she was imagining him ten years younger in her mind's eye, and beginning to understand a little more about the man he had grown into. 'And girls?'

'Of course,' he shrugged. 'Cars and girls, like any young pup. Trouble is,' his eyes glinted, 'I only remember the names of the cars.'

'Huh. Were you a good driver by then?'

'Sure. I'd won a few races, but that didn't bring much money in. By my early twenties that anger was starting to wear off.' He looked around the room, as though looking into a past world. 'All that wandering in my childhood had made me long for something permanent. A house, land, stability. But I didn't have any money, and I didn't have any qualifications.'

'So you took up test-driving?'

'Exactly. I had my heart set on Riverside Lodge, and I calculated it would take me two years to save up the deposit on it. I spent those two years crashing German cars and praying that no one else would see the potential in Riverside Lodge, and jump in before me.' He grinned, suddenly boyish. 'No one did. I bought the place—and, well, you know the rest.'

'You make it sound very simple, Con,' Gala sighed.

'Nothing in this life is simple.' He closed the album, turning to her. 'Not even falling in love.' She'd worn her hair loose today, and now he reached out to brush the auburn sweep of it away from her cheek. The words and the intimate gesture brought back flaring memories of that night at the Serafina—and a bitter recollection that this was to be their final encounter. She had to keep reminding herself that it wasn't love he wanted! She pulled away as though his touch had scalded her.

'You were going to show me your cars,' she said hastily, trying to break the spell that seemed to have fallen over them.

'You have a marvellous knack of changing the subject whenever it comes down to you and me.'

Damnably intelligent, his eyes assessed her. 'By now you must have some idea how I feel about you, Gala, yet you still play the whiptail lizard.'

'Just because you've taken a fancy for my body,' Gala said tartly, 'doesn't mean I have to leap into the nearest bed with you.'

'By God, you say some weird things.' For a moment the anger in his face made her quail, then it was gone. He stared into her eyes for long seconds, as though looking into her very soul, then rose. 'Okay. Let's go and see the cars.'

There were fifteen of them, all racing-cars, gleaming under the clear canopy of what had once been a barn, now converted into a spotless garage deep in the bottom of the garden. But although paintwork and chrome shone like new, and the whole place had an expensive smell of oil and leather and polish, Gala could tell that some of these cars were very old. The vintage cars were easy to spot; less easy were the sleek designs of the '50s and '60s, almost modern in their aerodynamic beauty.

Con led her through the silent, poised ranks. '1951 Ferrari four-and-a-half litre. My father raced that car. The long red job is another Ferrari, a Daytona. I still drive that one regularly. This is an Aston Martin DB IV—James Bond owned one, if you remember, but I don't think he could afford one on a Civil Service salary these days.' They paused in front of a truly old car, a silver-painted bullet with spoked wheels and great brass headlamps, trimmed with polished wood. 'That's a special Itala forty horse-power racer. The latest thing in speed in 1907.' He patted the bonnet affectionately. 'She belongs in a museum, really.'

'Do you look after all these creatures yourself?' Gala asked, staring around the amazing place.

'I haven't the time,' Con said regretfully. 'A man called Bob Jennings looks after them for me. I met him in the army—a real wizard with anything mechanical.'

'And they're all still running?'

'Pick one,' Con invited with a smile, 'and we'll take a ride in it after lunch.'

'Really?' Gala surveyed the cars with excited eyes. They all looked so exciting, so special. Finally, she pointed at a futuristic creation in racing red with tinted windows. 'That one looks the meanest machine of the lot.'

'It's a Lancia Stratos. My personal favourite. And an eminently suitable choice for you to have made.'

Something in his voice made her glance at him. 'Why suitable?'

'Because it's like you. Beautiful, illogical, temperamental . . .' He grinned. 'And utterly desirable. Shall we have some lunch?'

The meal was tranquil, and beautifully served by the smiling Mrs Belling. Con encouraged her to talk about her own childhood, his attentive eyes seeming to miss nothing. As before, he had the magical ability to smooth out her rough edges. Whether it was some mastery in him, or her own growing emotion, he could have her purring like a contented tabby—instead of the spitting thing she wanted to be!

Again, too, she found it perilously easy to slip into the dream that this was how it ought to be, this calm, growing love inside her. It was too painful to keep facing the realisation that this was to be their last meeting. It was much easier to simply pretend.

And yet, she thought, watching his face, the same trap was lurking there. The trap of sorting out what was real from what was only illusion.

And as they walked down to the garage afterwards, to get the Lancia for her promised ride, it was natural for her to nestle against him, demanding his arm around her waist again.

'You are a cat,' he said softly. 'You won't let anyone touch you until you've been fed.'

'I'll permit you to call me temperamental and illogical,' she said, the fine wine and good food having warmed her inhibitions into temporary sleep. 'Cats and women sometimes are. But I'm not mercenary.' She grinned up at him.

'Do you know how lovely you are when you smile?' he asked, the husky note in his voice sending a shiver down her back. 'With those jade-green eyes and that golden-red hair, you're as exquisite as a Fabergé jewel.'

'Do you flatter all your women like that?' she asked a little breathlessly.

'You are my only woman,' he said softly. 'If you want to put it that way. And the truth is no flattery. If I wanted to flatter you I'd say you were something you're not.'

'Such as?' she asked, falling into the trap.

'Easy to understand,' he said wryly. 'Come on.'

The roar of the Lancia's engine was unexpectedly savage, reeking of power. 'Music,' Con grinned. He eased the car out on to the drive. A touch of a button had the electric garage doors sliding closed behind them. 'Better buckle up.'

'You aren't going to drive fast, are you?' Gala asked with a touch of last-minute nerves.

'Not faster than the makers recommend.'

She settled back into the bucket-seats, feeling very low off the ground. 'How fast is that?'

'Name a figure, then double it.' The vicious acceleration sucked her back against the leather as the car surged out into the quiet street, and directed its mechanical thunder towards Oxfordshire.

CHAPTER SEVEN

AFTER the blur and the thrusting roar of a staggeringly fast drive, the woods were almost dreamlike. Their peace was deep, silent. By unspoken mutual consent, Con parked the Stratos on a deserted stretch of road, and they walked down through the trees, the thick carpet of last autumn's leaves rustling crisply underfoot. Her hand was linked through his, their fingers entwined. The late afternoon sunlight dappled through the tracery of branches overhead, warming them where it touched, but leaving cool pools of shadow that still smelled and tasted of winter.

Apart from the few wood-pigeons that spluttered into life ahead of them, the solitude was unbroken. At the edge of a stream so glassy that it seemed to be barely moving, they stopped, enchanted by the magic of the place. Gala laid her head on Con's shoulder, half-closing her eyes.

'I wish it could always be like this,' she sighed. 'I wish today would never end.'

'It doesn't have to end,' he said gently. He turned to face her, cupping her face in his hands. 'You and I don't have to end, Gala.'

'Yes we do,' she said sadly, thinking of Jack.

His kiss tasted bittersweet to her, as though the sadness of the sunset had come between them. His eyes, deep and beautiful as the sea, smiled at her. 'Why? You and I have our lifetimes ahead of us, Gala.'

'What are you saying?' she asked, feeling the ache pass through her soul.

'I'm saying that you mean a great deal to me, Gala. More than any woman I've ever known.' His voice was compelling, urgent. 'I want more from you than kisses. More than just sex. I want you, your heart and your soul. For ever.'

'Oh . . .' On the verge of sudden tears, Gala pulled his hands away. 'You're breaking my heart, Con. Don't.'

'Is there some reason why you can't give me those things?' he demanded. 'If there is, for God's sake tell me. You know there's nothing that couldn't be resolved, nothing that couldn't be forgiven.'

'There's no reason. Not the sort of reason that can be helped, anyway.'

'Is it that you don't feel anything for me?' he asked quietly. 'That I don't touch you?'

'*Yes.*' She turned away from him, and walked blindly away from the ripple of the stream. 'Yes,' she said shakily, 'that's exactly it. I don't love you, I never could. It's all a waste of time.' The distant note of a bird was the only sound in the deep stillness. Then, pain searing her, Gala spun round with glistening eyes. 'Oh, Con, you know that's a lie. I feel for you . . . so much. So much that I can't bear it sometimes.'

He almost smiled at her contradictory statements. 'Then for God's sake, why all this?'

'Because I don't trust you.'

He walked towards her, taking her hands in his, shaking his head. 'But why not?'

'Because you're amoral. Because you don't have any conscience.' She gulped. 'Because I'll just be another conquest to you, to be lain with and forgotten in a few weeks.' His fingers bit hard into her pulses, making her gasp. His expression was more bitter than she'd ever seen it.

'How dare you?' he said in a deathly quiet voice. Tears filled her green eyes, dulling their sparkle. 'What damned right do you have to say things like that?'

She couldn't get her hands free, and had to twist her head down to wipe her tears away on her upper arm. As though the touchingly childish gesture had moved him, he slowly released her hands, and watched her silently as she dug in her pocket and fumbled for a tissue to dry her swollen lids.

'You think what I'm offering you is just pure lust, then?' he asked quietly.

'Con,' she said in a husky voice, not looking at him, 'you don't understand. I've been trying so hard to get away from you. For days and weeks. Not because I hate you—but because I'm just too susceptible to you. I simply can't trust you, not ever, because of the man you are.' She looked up, meeting eyes as cold as a Northern winter. 'I'm in a cleft stick, and it hurts. More than someone as strong as you can know. Please, please believe me—I don't ever want to see you again. Not ever. I meant what I said at the Serafina that night. This is the last time between us, the last ever.' She stood back on legs that threatened to give way, her eyes continually blurring with tears. 'Oh, Con, I'm so sorry,' she whispered.

'Gala!'

Grief was almost too big to fit in her heart then, and she walked away, tears spilling through her fingers.

'Don't,' she said in a choked voice, hearing the rustle of his footsteps following her. 'If you care anything at all for me, just leave me alone.'

'Don't be childish,' he said coolly. 'Let me drive you back to your flat.'

'*No*. Don't follow me, *please*.' Crazily, she started running, the leaves crunching red and yellow and gold under her feet. Her hair tumbled loose, cascading as red as autumn itself down her back.

Like some wounded creature, she needed the dark shelter of the woods, needed to be away from eyes that would see her pain. Down the bank, through the

gnarled trunks, into the twilight that glimmered
between the silent trees. The woods blurred around
her, the network of branches dancing jerkily as she
ran.

She ran a long way. Sobbing for breath, she finally
stumbled against a holly-bush, the only green thing in
the woods, and felt the leathery leaves clutch at her,
piercing the linen of her clothes like needles. She sank
against a felled tree nearby, turning to look the way
she'd come. There was no sign of Con. Deeply
grateful that he hadn't followed, she rested her head
against the rough bark, and gave way to her emotion.

Yes, it was crazy, yes it was irrational, but that was
what she'd needed to do. To get away, to hide and cry
like this. Damn Jack, damn Crystal Warren, damn the
Fates and the bitter ironies they seemed to love so
much.

The cold and the silence sank slowly into her,
leaving her drained of tears. The twilight was turning
into evening, and an aching loneliness reminded her
that she was a long, long way from home. She stood
up, trying to brush leaves and moss from her skirt,
feeling drained. Through the trees ahead of her she
could see what looked like another road. Slowly, she
walked down towards it. It was deserted.

Desolate and a little afraid, she huddled into her
thin jacket. By now Con would be half-way to
London, cursing her for her woman's foibles. About a
mile or two down the road she could see a grey blob
that might be a bus-shelter. Maybe she'd be able to
get a bus back to London. She set off, the isolation of
the leafless, wintry landscape almost bringing back her
tears. This was the perfect end to a perfect day, all
right.

A glimmer of headlights behind made her heart
jump with the expectation that it might be Con. But
the car was an aged Maxi. It slowed down, though,

and stopped beside her. The driver, a grey-haired
woman, looked out at Gala in concern.

'You all right?'

'Yes, fine,' she said tiredly. 'Do you know where I
can get a bus into London, please?'

'I'm going into London now.' The accent was
clipped, upper-class. 'You don't want to be wandering
round the woods at this time of the day, young lady.
Jump in, I'll give you a lift.'

'Oh,' Gala sighed in heartfelt thanks, 'that would be
lovely.' She leaned back, exhausted, as the little car
puttered on its way. The old lady's eyes were still
creased with concern.

'Has something happened to you?'

'It's all too silly and sad to talk about,' Gala said,
her voice dreamy and disconnected. Or perhaps she
merely thought she said the words, for sleep had
stolen up unawares, and she sank into it gratefully.

CHAPTER EIGHT

GETTING home took the edge off her grief, helping her to harden her resolve that this had to be, indeed, the end. The terminus. When it came to deciding between Con and her family, there could be, surely, only one choice—to cut Con out of her life completely.

If life was like a romantic film, she reflected bitterly, she'd probably have consigned her family to the devil, and chosen Con. Con and love. If only it were as easy as that! But that kind of conviction just wasn't possible when she couldn't trust the man who so attracted her. To be a romantic heroine you had to be utterly sure of your man, and she wasn't, never would be. The issue raised by Crystal wasn't just a matter of family loyalty. It was a vital indicator of Conrad Brandon's personality.

And what if Crystal Warren hadn't stood between them? If she hadn't had that very concrete evidence of Con's fundamental irresponsibility and callousness, how would she have reacted to him?

The thought haunted her that night, but by the next morning she'd managed to persuade herself that even without her knowledge of what had happened to Crystal she'd have felt the same deep unease about Con. For one thing, the whole situation was simply too good to be true.

Dazzling men like Con didn't fall in love with mousy women like herself. The level of interest she roused in him, she was sure, fell far short of her own passion for him. Perhaps she intrigued him. All that Ice Princess stuff probably piqued his male pride. But once he had conquered, what then?

Wouldn't she be discarded, like any other toy that had begun to bore?

For another thing, their worlds were so remote. She'd had a perfectly ordinary upbringing. *His* childhood had been anything but ordinary. He'd told her so himself. Wildly romantic, but hardly the sort of upbringing to foster a steady, responsible personality! You couldn't expect someone brought up in the roar and colour of the racing world to have ordinary attitudes, ordinary moral standards. You wouldn't choose a Formula One racing car as the family saloon.

And *that* line of thought led her to one stark question: what did she want out of love? A soothing Sunday drive in a family saloon? Or the thrilling, dangerous exhilaration that Con seemed able to unleash?

'The truth is,' she sighed to herself, 'that I'm a dull person who likes a dull, peaceful life.'

She repeated that once more to persuade herself she meant it.

Yes, she decided, she was doing the right thing. Not only the right thing as regarded her family, but the right thing for her own happiness. And though the decision tore at her, she made up her mind on that Monday that she would rebuff any attempt Con made to get back in touch with her.

That Con didn't contact her again for several days spoiled her plans, though. At first she was longing for him to ring or call, just so that she could deliver the monumental snub she had all planned. And by doing so, prove her loyalty to Jack. And prove that she wasn't, after all, completely under Con's spell.

Then she found she was longing just to find his writing in her letterbox, hear his deep voice on the 'phone, or see his face. Aching for his touch in a way that had nothing to do with loyalty to Jack or her parents. It also began to occur to her that someone with Con Brandon's charisma could have any woman he wanted. After the way she'd rebuffed him, why the hell should he even bother with her? She thought of the diamonds that sparkled between Coral Bonnington's neat, tanned breasts, and discovered a capacity for blazing jealousy.

By Friday evening all her longings and fears had dulled into hopelessness.

She spent the week-end at her parents' house, leaving Pasha with the retired couple downstairs. Sleeping in her old narrow bed didn't ease her dreams.

Jack came round on Sunday morning, and it was almost like old times. No-one mentioned Con's name, though much that was unspoken hovered rather oppressively on the air, and Gala was grateful to be left alone. She'd been feeling so strange, as though she were changing inside—and not necessarily for the better, either. The glossy newness of her life seemed to have suddenly been tarnished, as though she'd become mature and cynical overnight.

The weepy black-and-white film on television that afternoon grated on her nerves until she felt she was going to scream, and as soon as she decently could, she said goodbye, got into her car, and drove back to London, her accelerator foot flat on the floorboards all the way. Leaving, she knew, a worried and suspicious brother and parents behind her. She didn't care. Let them think what they liked. She had enough troubles of her own without a beady-eyed family to think about as well.

There was only one cure, she knew, for this horribly on-edge feeling. And that was to see Con, one last time, and talk to him. Try and explain some of the complex reasons behind her apparently mad behaviour, and say a proper goodbye. If she hadn't been such a coward about pain, she'd have spoken to him weeks ago.

Yes, it was slavish and contemptible to think of going to him. It was like admitting defeat. But the very thought of seeing him again had her heart thumping in her chest. Would this yearning for him ever leave her? She took a deep breath, and instead of turning off for Wandsworth, she headed straight on for the city, guessing he'd be at the Serafina at this time on a Sunday evening.

She found a parking place in the street outside, and taking her courage in both hands, walked into the foyer.

'Mr Brandon doesn't usually see guests at this time,' the receptionist informed her from behind her polished mahogany counter. 'Would you like to leave a message?'

'This is a personal call,' Gala persisted. 'Please tell him it's Miss Fletcher. I'm sure he'll see me.' In her after-work jeans and woolly jumper she wasn't exactly the acme of sophistication, and the receptionist's immaculately made up eyes flicked doubtfully up and down her figure.

'He really doesn't like to be disturbed...' She broke off as a slim, dark figure in a beautifully cut charcoal suit materialised at her elbow.

'Why, hello, Gala,' Coral Bonnington smiled. 'What can we do for you?'

'The young lady wanted to see Mr Brandon,' the receptionist said. 'I was just telling her that he's always busy during four and six on a Sunday...'

'Never mind, Jill, I'll deal with this.' Coral came round the counter to meet Gala. 'Con's in his office, doing some paperwork. But I'm sure he'll want to see you, so I'll take you to him.'

'Thank you.' Gala walked with Coral across the lobby. 'That's a beautiful outfit,' she couldn't help saying.

'Con bought it for me on one of his trips to Italy,'

Coral replied, giving her another smile. 'He's got superb taste.'

Jealousy raked Gala's nerves. 'Indeed he has,' she said, but Coral didn't seem to notice the acid in her tone.

'I'm sorry you weren't feeling well the other night,' she went on. 'We missed you. Your friend Richard stayed until two a.m.'

'Did he?' Gala tried to force joviality into her voice. 'I hope he didn't make a nuisance of himself?'

'I usually stay up that late anyway. My job, you see. I'm a night-owl.' She ushered Gala through a leather-padded door. 'It was nice to have someone to keep me company for a change.'

'Oh?' Gala gave Coral a tight smile, almost hating this polished young beauty. 'Doesn't Con usually keep you occupied during the wee hours?' she asked pointedly.

'I'm a member of staff here,' she replied obliquely, unoffended. 'Con is the owner. I work what hours he tells me to.'

'I'm sure you do,' Gala said nastily. 'You're his right-hand woman. Who's his left-hand woman?'

'I'm not Con's lover, Gala,' Coral replied in the same mild voice. 'You don't have to be my enemy.'

'Oh, hell.' In the softly lit corridor, Gala touched Coral's arm with a sigh. 'I'm so sorry, Coral. That was unforgivable of me. I'm all on edge, and I've just discovered that I'm rather a bitch.'

'Con usually has that effect on the women around him.' Coral said. Her smile was genuine, but had her tone been bittersweet? Gala stopped, turning to face Coral.

'Coral . . .' The words faltered on her lips. The dark girl's mouth descended in a wry curve.

'You want to know whether I've ever been Con's lover?'

'Something like that,' Gala confessed unhappily. 'I'm desperate for advice, you see.'

'I don't give advice. And I don't listen to any, either.' Coral leaned against the wall, her hands clasped behind her back. 'When I came to work here a few years ago, I was a very confused kid. I'm not that anymore. I've got things I never dreamed of—beautiful clothes, a good career, a wonderful boss, a lifestyle that's always exciting, always different. All that is thanks to Con Brandon.' She was the epitome of an elegant, cosmopolitan figure, and Gala thought suddenly of the raving punk she'd once been. 'If I were in love with Con, Gala, I'd know that I was jeopardising my position.' She tilted her dark head. 'Do you understand what I mean? I would cease to become an employee—in more senses than one. And I want my job badly. So if I were ever unlucky enough to fall in love with Con Brandon, I'd make sure I hid it so deep that he'd never ever find it.'

For long seconds, Gala stared into Coral's sloe-black eyes, trying to fathom this self-sufficient, neat personality. Was there pain in those lustrous almond eyes? Or just the calm of a dedicated career woman? Coral's soft laugh broke the spell.

'I'm sorry, I'm keeping you from the person you came to see. He's just this way.' She led Gala to the end of the corridor, and pushed open an oak door. 'Gala's here, Con.' To Gala she murmured, 'Good luck, whatever you're hoping for,' and walked back, her high heels click-clicking down the corridor. Gala pushed through the door.

The only light in the darkened room came from the reading-lamp on Con's desk. It threw his face into half-light, emphasising his harshly masculine good looks, glancing gold off the pen in his hand, and pooling shadows in the white silk of his shirt. His eyes met hers, clear grey and cold as ice.

'The prodigal returns,' he said softly, capping the pen and leaning back.

'I had to talk to you,' she said. Her throat was suddenly dry as she closed the door behind her. He looked very forbidding indeed, and utterly remote from the pagan lover who'd set her senses on fire, or the relaxed companion of that blissful Sunday. Now he was every inch the ruthless man of affairs again, highly successful and ultra-competitive. 'I'm sorry if I'm disturbing you.'

'It's time for a whisky, anyway.' He nodded at the cabinet. 'In there.' Gala obeyed. As she found the whisky among the bottles and squirted soda into both crystal tumblers, Con went on casually, 'Do I take it you've come for a post-mortem on Sunday's fiasco?'

'Partly,' she nodded. She lowered her eyes. 'I got home all right, by the way. A lady gave me a lift.'

'In a Maxi, I know. I followed you.' She lowered her eyes in embarrassment, and he drummed his fingers on the desk-top. 'You're a bit of a puzzle, Gala. If you'd been a man, some of the things you've said and done to me over the past few weeks would have landed you in hospital. As it is, I can shrug most of them off.' He paused. 'Not all of them, but most of them.' He took the glass from her, lifted it in an ironic toast, and gulped a third of it down. 'I have a feeling I'm about to discover what it's all about. Sit down.'

She sat in the leather-bound armchair, bracing herself. A vision of their naked embrace flashed hot and salty through her mind. How strange it was to be talking now in this cold, hostile way. The whisky's warmth sank into her stomach, and she met his eyes levelly.

'I don't suppose you'd even remember a girl called Crystal Warren?' she asked in a quiet voice.

'Crystal?' He cupped the tumbler thoughtfully in his palm. 'Yes, I remember her. But what . . .' He broke off, eyes darkening with knowledge. 'God! Is *that* what's at the bottom of this?'

'Yes.'

'Crystal Warren and Jack Fletcher.' His voice was soft. The piercing eyes were introspective now, looking inwards, not at Gala. '*Damn*. Why didn't I connect the names? I've been racking my brain for weeks, and I never once thought of that.'

'I don't suppose it meant all that much to you,' Gala suggested ironically. Now that it was out, her mood seemed to have shifted from nervous fear to weariness. 'But you see, Jack's my brother, and what you did to him hurt him very badly indeed.'

'Your brother.' He was looking into the past with smoky eyes. 'There was another brother, a pilot . . .'

'Mike,' she nodded. 'You made us all suffer. My brothers, my parents—and me.'

'I see.' His voice was very quiet. 'But I didn't do anything to your brother, Gala. It wasn't my fault.'

'That's what I expected you to say.' Feeling distinctly ill, Gala rubbed a stain the bottom of her glass had left on the leather-bound arm of the chair. 'In a way I think you almost believe that it wasn't your fault. You're just too damned attractive, Con. It must be so easy for you. Like it was with me. The thing is that I'm free.' She looked up wryly. 'To all intents and purposes, anyway. But you shouldn't have done it to Crystal. It was cruel and destructive. And that's why I've been trying not to get involved with you. Because no matter how charming you are, I know you for what you are. I know the *real* Con Brandon.' She got up, feeling there was nothing more to say except goodbye. 'I just wanted you to know that.'

'*Sit down.*' His face was fiercely angry, his sensual mouth a grim line. 'You're way off base, Gala. You're bursting with prejudices and dislikes which have grown out of something you don't even remotely understand.'

'I understand what happened to my brother,' she said, her voice starting to shake with anger and unhappiness. 'I understand what you did to Crystal Warren.'

'You were just a child,' he rasped. 'What the hell do you know about it?'

'I was nearly twenty-one! Old enough to understand!' God, she felt wretched. In that moment it came to her that she cared a damn sight more for Con Brandon than she'd even realised. 'You've got a way with words, you could wrap me round your finger if I listened to you. That's why I'm not going to . . .'

'Your brother was well out of it,' he cut through her sentence. 'He was a damned fool to even consider marrying Crystal.'

'Don't you *dare* call Jack a fool,' Gala hissed, ready to throw something at his tanned face. 'He ought to have beaten you—like a dog!'

'He ought to have tried,' Con said silkily. 'He didn't have the courage, though.'

'No, because he's got the decency *you* so obviously lack,' she shot back, eyes glinting seafire.

'He was so decent that he needed a nursemaid,' he said cuttingly. 'Crystal was running after me like a cat on heat, Gala. A week later it was someone else.'

'You're amazing, you know that? Do you really imagine I'd ever believe that you took Crystal away from Jack as an act of *benevolence*?'

'I didn't take Crystal at all,' he said quietly.

'Liar!'

His eyes glittered. 'Don't you ever call me that again, you little whelp.'

'Are you denying it?'

'It was a long time ago.' Cat-like, his pupils expanded into dark pools. 'Maybe I did. And if I did—do you really think Jack ought to have married Crystal?'

The question took her unawares. 'He loved Crystal,' she said unsteadily. 'Something you wouldn't understand, *Mr* Brandon. He still loves her.'

'Yeah. Like I said—he's a damned fool.'

'I'm going,' she said, blinded by tears.

'Do you know how many men Crystal Warren had before Jack?' he pursued, ignoring her swimming eyes. 'Do you know how many she's had since Jack?'

'I don't want to hear your horrible lies!'

'I'm not going to comment on Crystal's character, because she's got her own problems. But she never gave a damn for your brother. How long do you think their marriage would have lasted? Would you really want your precious Jack to go through the trauma of a broken marriage?'

'You're disgusting.'

'And you're ridiculous. You're all wrong about me and Crystal.'

'I don't believe a word you say.' Anger dried her tears for a second. 'You know how to get your own way. But if you ever come near me again, my brother will . . .'

'Will what?' he prompted acidly. 'Hit me with his handbag?'

'He'll call the police,' she finished on a trembling note. Con's eyes widened for a second, and then he leaned back, laughing softly with genuine amusement.

'My dear Gala, I wouldn't come near you again if you were the last woman in London.' His voice was a velvety whiplash. 'Your honour is quite safe, I assure you. Scotland Yard can rest easy.' Languidly, he uncapped his pen, and leaned forward to his papers. 'Was there anything else?'

Grasping her bag with nerveless fingers, Gala could only stare at his unemotional face.

'No,' she said at last, her voice little more than a whisper. 'There's nothing else.'

'Then I wish you goodbye.' Indifferently, he bent to his work again. Gala turned to the door, and stumbled out into the corridor, feeling utterly stunned by what had happened.

In her car she rested her forehead sickly on the steering-wheel, closing her eyes. She'd done what she came here to do. Now it was all over. She'd expected arguments, bitterness—but not that glacial indifference at the end. If he'd shown any sign of being hurt, paradoxically, she'd have felt a hundred times less desolate. But to think that she really *had* meant nothing to him, that all the excitement and desire had been on her part alone——

A rap at her window made her lift her head. The two policemen outside were peering in with concerned young faces.

'You all right, Miss?' one asked as she wound the window down.

'I'm fine,' she nodded, dredging up a smile. 'I just felt a little faint.'

'Only we saw you'd had a bump.' The other policeman pointed to her dented headlamp. 'Thought you might have been injured.'

'Oh, no. It's all right, thank you.' She wiped the tears hastily off her cheeks, feeling a complete fool. 'I'm much better now.'

'Sure?'

'Absolutely. Thanks for asking.'

'No trouble.' They strolled on, their black capes shiny with the drizzle that had begun to fall. Gala started her car, and drove out into the street, unable to get rid of the lump in her throat.

Something else had been hard to bear as well. The disappointment. Disappointment that he hadn't answered her back. Somehow she'd been hoping against hope that the whole thing had been some terrible mistake. When she'd told him who she was, she'd been almost expecting him to defend himself. To offer some explanation, however unlikely, for his elopment with Crystal. Instead he'd denied it coolly and tersely, and that had only made it worse.

Well, she'd done right by her family, done right by all the conventions that dictated what a well-brought up young physiotherapist in a starched white smock ought to do.

Now maybe they'd all leave her in peace to mourn over the ashes of what might have been.

The water was delicious, and a clear, tropical blue to counteract the grey skies that lowered overhead. The vast crystal dome kept the weather safely out, though, and it was greenhouse-warm, as always.

'Kick, Tarquin.' Gala backed slowly, pulling the spluttering child with her as he moved his legs in an unco-ordinated frog kick. Sonia McRae, in her old-fashioned frilly bathing-costume, watched from the edge of the pool. The other mothers, under Gala's watchful eye, were leading their own children through the same exercise. 'Kick. Harder!'

'I'm *trying*.' Not looking as though he were enjoying himself very much, Tarquin swallowed a mouthful of water and coughed indignantly. To him the pool was a play-area, and he could never understand why so much of his time here had to be organised into unpleasant exercises. Hydrotherapy was an invaluable aid, though, and one which Gala had come to rely on more and more. The water made paraplegic children like Tarquin and his class almost weightless, allowing them a freedom of movement they almost never got on land.

'Now back again. And when you reach the other side,' Gala promised, 'you can play as long as you like.' Through his plastered-down fringe Tarquin's eyes brightened, and he kicked out manfully. The long, slow progress was accomplished at last, and Sonia took charge of a tired but triumphant boy. Gala guided the other mothers through the last part of the exercise, and then declared the class over.

There was time to relax before her next patient. She hauled herself out of the water, and sat on the edge, tilting her head to let her sheet of auburn hair drain. The turquoise one-piece that clung to her wet body revealed that she'd lost weight. In the past four or five days, she'd eaten barely a thing. Her appetite had gone. And with it, she decided glumly, looking down, her bust was going too. Her nipples poked plaintively up from breasts the size of a schoolgirl's, and her long legs seemed longer and slimmer than ever.

'Been on diet?' Gala looked up to see Alanna Cipriani smiling down at her. 'You're deliciously trim.'

'You mean painfully thin, but thanks. Shouldn't you be in your surgery?'

'I've got an hour off, so I thought I'd read through some reports in the sun.' She glanced at the children splashing around in the water. 'Been taking your paraplegics?'

'Yes.' Gala squeezed water out of her hair, and leaned back. She felt tired. She was always tired these days. She gave Alanna a wan smile. 'Got anything for an instant pick-me-up?'

'I'd recommend a stiff gin, but it's barely three.' Alanna squatted gingerly next to Gala, clutching her reports to her bosom. 'Are you okay?' she asked concernedly. 'You've been like the walking dead this week.'

'A touch of 'flu,' Gala lied. 'It makes you feel so wretched.'

'I'll prescribe some antibiotics for you if you want,' her friend offered, but Gala shook her head.

'I'll be all right, Alanna, thanks.'

'Want to call off tonight's squash?'

'No, the exercise will probably do me good.'

'Well, take a few days off if you feel like it. No sense in driving yourself when you're not well.' She paused. 'A little bird told me,' she went on casually, 'that you've been going out with Con Brandon.'

'There are a damn sight too many little birds around,' Gala said explosively, 'all with great big ears and great big eyes.'

'Hmm! I thought you were protesting too much the other night!' Alanna's dark eyes took in Gala's pale, thin cheeks. 'Still, after all the things you were saying about Con, I found it a little hard to believe you'd be going around with him——'

'Well, I'm not any more,' Gala said shortly, her nerves jumping.

'Oh.' Alanna put a lot of understanding into the monosyllable. 'So *that's* the way it is.'

'It isn't any way.' Gala scooped up her towel and blotted the sad pink leaf of her mouth. 'I suppose your "little bird" was Richard Schwarzmuller?' Alanna nodded, and Gala silently cursed Richard's talkative nature. 'All that happened was that Richard took me out to this hotel.' She grimaced. 'Which happened to belong to Con Brandon. He saw us there, insisted on muscling in, and thoroughly spoiled our evening.'

'Not according to Richard.' Alanna's pretty face was alight with amusement. 'He was most impressed with Con—and some little assistant of his called Coral something.'

'Con got Richard drunk,' Gala said wearily. 'Richard wouldn't have noticed if Con had set a bomb off under his chair.'

Alanna gurgled with laughter. 'He always was a pirate. You do have to admire his style, though.'

'Do I?' Gala asked frigidly.

'Well, at least it shows he's taken quite a fancy to you,' Alanna said enviously. 'You have all the luck, Gala.'

'Not any more,' Gala said drily. 'I've made sure that Con's brand of luck doesn't ever come my way again.'

'You turned him down?'

'Oh, Alanna.' Gala found she had the heart for a slight smile at her friends' astonishment. 'Just because you think he's wonderful doesn't mean everyone else has to think so as well. Yes, I turned him down.'

'Because of this mysterious feud you've got going with him?'

'Basically, yes.'

'Wow.' Alanna shook her dark head. 'You wouldn't be looking this miserable if you didn't care for him at least a little, though.'

'Wrong tense.'

'Eh?'

'You've got the wrong tense.' Gala stood up, wrapping her towel around her slender body. 'Not *care*. *Cared*. Past imperfect. I don't care a damn about him any more.' Open-mouthed, Alanna watched her leave, an exquisitely slim figure with golden-red hair that the water had darkened to bronze.

'Gala!'

Gala didn't look back, not wanting Alanna to see that her green eyes were wet. 'See you tonight,' she called. And disappeared into the cool white retreat of the changing-rooms.

'Time for our daily dose of sado-masochism, Miss Fletcher?'

'Good morning, Mr Bullen,' she replied coolly. He'd been making the same joke ever since he'd arrived at the Clinic, and it was wearing a little thin now.

'Come on, Gala,' he grinned, sitting down uninvited on the edge of her desk, 'don't be so frosty. I could quite fancy you in black leather, with a whip.'

'I don't find that very funny,' she said in the same unamused tone. 'Roll your sleeve up, please.'

'Cor, they were right when they called you the Ice Princess,' he chuckled, obeying.

'When *who* called me the Ice Princess?' she enquired grimly.

'Just people.' Len Bullen tipped her a sly wink. 'Plenty of people think very highly of you, so never mind about the Ice Princess bit. Did I tell you that a pal of mine recommended me to see you?'

'Frequently,' Gala replied drily.

'Yeah, Bertie Naylor. Claimed you worked wonders with him.'

'Well, let's see what we can work with you,' Gala said, mollified a little.

'This is called manipulation, ain't it?' he leered. 'When I tell my fiancée that you give me manipulation three times a week she practically goes wild.'

'Oh, grow up,' she told him snappishly. Sorry as she felt for Len Bullen and his damaged hand, she sometimes loathed his sense of humour. Bullen, balding, jowly and striving after youth, was a successful salesman, but Gala guessed he would never shake off the bar-room vulgarity of his young days as a very minor rep. She liked the bustling little man, but he wasn't the sort of patient to deal with in the middle of a major depression.

'Temper, temper,' he said coquettishly. 'Anyone would think you'd been crossed in love or something.' Her vivid green eyes flicked up angrily to his. 'Don't bite my head off,' he interjected before she could speak. 'When a gorgeous creature like you goes around with a face like thunder all day long, there's bound to be some geezer at the bottom of it.'

'We don't have all day, Mr Bullen.' He'd touched her on the raw. These past two weeks had been the bleakest period she'd ever known. She thrust the all-too-familiar vicious circle of thought away, and addressed herself to Len Bullen. The accident which had damaged vital muscles and tendons in his arm had left his right hand almost useless, and it was going to take years for him to get anything like proper use back. 'Try and squeeze my hand,' she commanded.

'Wouldn't I love to,' he said wistfully. His too-red face tightened as he tried to move the limp, cold fingers that lay in her own. She could almost see the brain sending furious impulses down the damaged nerveways, trying to drive a path through the scar-tissue that blocked the neurons off. The faint quivering was pathetic, but it was a hopeful sign. 'That's all I can manage,' he groaned.

'It's not bad,' Gala reassured him. 'In time it'll get a lot better.

'In time?' His joviality deserted him for a moment as he stared at her capable hands manipulating his fingers. 'You mean weeks?'

'I mean years, and you know it.' She smiled sympathetically, and tapped his little finger. 'Try and move that one.'

'I'm getting married in a few month's time, you know.' He inspected the immobile digit morosely. 'A one-handed man doesn't make much of a lover.'

'I'm sure your fiancée will make allowances.' She was more interested in his tendons. If the important ones had been completely severed, the salesman was going to need a graft if he was ever to move his hand properly. 'Try and move the next one, please.'

'My Chris is a very demanding lady,' he informed Gala. 'She doesn't make too many allowances. Hey, that reminds me. When I mentioned your name to her she thought she might know you.'

'Really?' Gala was wondering whether to mention the slight bruising still apparent on his wrist to Sir Lionel. Any obstruction to the blood-supply might be contributing to Len Bullen's loss of function.

'Yeah—said she'd known your brother years ago.'

Gala looked up. 'You say her name's Chris?'

'Chris Warren.'

'*Crystal?*'

'That's what she calls herself,' Len Bullen smiled. 'But I just call her Chris. It gets on her nerves, I can tell you.'

'You? Getting married to Crystal Warren?' Gala said, shaken.

Len flushed an even deeper shade of brick. 'I know I'm a bit older than she is. But, well—girls prefer the older man, don't they? More experience and all that.' He looked dejectedly down. 'If only I hadn't crocked this hand of mine . . .'

'But I thought Crystal was in America . . .' Hearing Crystal's name drop from this man's mouth had thrown Gala badly off-balance. It was too soon after her traumatic experiences with Con Brandon for her to meet the revelation with any equanimity. 'How—how long have you been engaged to her?'

'Oh, months. She *was* in America, for a couple of years. Very successful, too, modelling for one of their biggest catalogues. But she missed the old country, so she came back. 'Course, she couldn't find the sort of cushy number she'd had over there.' Len winked broadly. 'Met her while she was working a club in the West End. Dead posh.'

'A club?'

'Hostess,' Len nodded. 'Ow, that doesn't half hurt!'

'Sorry,' Gala apologised. 'Can you do the exercise I showed you?'

'I'll try.'

'A hostess,' Gala repeated, watching the meaty hand trying to slowly curl and uncurl on the table.

'Yeah. Bit of a come-down for her, know what I mean? Still, she's well out of it now.'

'She's left the club?'

'Retired,' Len nodded proudly. 'I've set her up in a little flat, haven't I? Bought her a nice motor, a Mini Metro, given her money for nice clothes and what have you. I mean, I couldn't have my intended working in a job like that, no matter how posh a place it was.'

'Sounds as though you've been very generous,' Gala said automatically. She reached absently for her case-notes. For a few seconds she hesitated, wondering whether she ought to re-open the whole can of worms. It didn't take her more than seconds to realise that she didn't really have any choice. She still cared far too much about Con to pass up a chance like this. 'Mr Bullen, d'you think she'd see me?'

'You mean like for a visit? 'Course she would,' Len said jovially. 'She's always complaining about not having any friends. Yeah, she'd love to see you.'

'D'you think so? There's so much I want to talk to her about.' She smiled at him. 'You can give that hand some more exercise, then, and write out her address for me.'

Len Bullen had been more than generous to his retired intended. As she got out of her car, later that evening, Gala almost envied Crystal these flats. Tucked away in a shrubby N.5 mews, they were well-maintained and compact. There was a neat little garden, and an enclosed parking-area where a dark-blue Mini Metro stood among the other cars. Clean and modern, the sort of place that was like gold in London nowadays.

Len had obviously worked hard to get her a flat as nice as this.

She walked along the open first-floor corridor and knocked at the varnished door of No 12, her heart beating slightly faster than normal. It opened, and a slim blonde woman stood framed in the doorway, fanning a set of freshly-painted scarlet fingernails.

'Yes?'

'Crystal, do you remember me? Gala Fletcher . . .'

'Jack's sister.' Animation lit the blue eyes. 'Of course I remember you. Hell, you've changed a lot since I last saw you!'

'You haven't.' It was true. Crystal was still the same pretty creature, her diminutive face and body well-groomed and well-cared-for. Large eyes, a bee-stung mouth, a pointed chin. 'Can I come in?'

'You might as well.' Crystal stood aside to let her in, and closed the door behind her. 'So how's Jack these days?'

'Fine.' Gala looked around. The flat had been neatly furnished and carpeted, but it was in rather sordid disorder. The television set was on, and a half-eaten plate of chips was on the carpet in front of it. 'Sorry, am I interrupting your dinner?'

'What? Oh, those are last night's.' Crystal perched herself on a chair and started painting the nails on her other hand. 'I suppose Len gave you the address?'

'Yes.' Gala found an armchair that wasn't covered in discarded clothes, and sat down. 'His hand's coming on quite well.'

'I call this place the Birdcage. Because he keeps me cooped up here.' Crystal admired her outspread fingers. 'You look prosperous. Physio-whatsit must pay.'

'Not a great deal,' Gala smiled. The television chattered on at half-volume. It was a bit disconcerting to meet Crystal after three years and get this rather off-hand welcome. There wasn't the slightest trace of shame or guilt in Crystal, either. 'You're lucky to have a fiancée as generous as Len.'

'Lucky?' Crystal capped the nail-varnish bottle. 'You must be joking. Len Bullen generous? He wouldn't give you the sweat off—he wouldn't give away a thing.'

Gala's eyebrows lifted in surprise. 'I thought he'd set this flat up for you?'

'Only so's he could claim sole rights over me.' Crystal pouted. 'This place is miles from anywhere. There's no nice clubs or pubs, no-one except nosey old parkers and silly fools walking their dogs. I'm cooped up here, I tell you.'

'Hasn't he bought you a car?' Gala probed.

'Big deal. A second-hand Mini Metro.' Scornfully, Crystal got up, fluttering her hand to dry the varnish. 'The ultimate big spender, our Len. Coffee?'

'Yes please.' Gala watched Crystal through the open-plan kitchen. The pretty face had a childish cast, as though it had never grown up.

'Let's face it,' Crystal went on, clattering cups, 'Len's no dreamboat. He's as common as muck, and he's way too old for me.'

'Why are you marrying him, then?' Gala asked.

'Force of circumstance.' Crystal pulled a sour face. 'I'm twenty-nine myself, you know. Soon I'll be too old to get married.'

'You're still very attractive,' Gala smiled.

'Ach! The face goes, then the boobs go, then everything goes.' She stared morosely at the kettle. 'At least Len's got money. He lives with his old Mum, can you beat it? Thick as two short planks, both of them. Anyway, I thought I was on to a good thing for a while.'

Gala shook her head slightly. 'And now you don't?'

'Well, I mean.' Amid clouds of steam, Crystal made

instant coffee for them both and brought it through. 'He's a bit of a fool, isn't he?'

'I like him.' Gala stirred her coffee. 'He's crazy about you.'

'Randy old goat.' She didn't smile as she said it. 'And now to top it all he's gone and done his hand in.' She looked up at Gala. 'Here, is he ever going to be able to use it again?'

'In a couple of years, maybe . . .'

'Oh, that's great, isn't it. A couple of *years*? And I've always had a thing about cripples!'

'He's not a cripple,' Gala said sharply. Crystal's callousness had surprised her. 'And he's still in a lot of pain.'

'Don't I know it,' Crystal yawned. 'He's always moaning on about it. He bores me stiff, frankly. He's a salesman and he'll always be a salesman. Common and tight-fisted. A nobody. A nothing.'

In silence, Gala glanced round the flat again. It looked more like a nineteen-year-old's than a twenty-nine-year-old's. The mess of records, soiled clothes and half-eaten food was faintly nauseating. She wondered whether Crystal could possibly have always been this sloppy, this shallow.

'Have you come to give me hell about your brother?' Crystal asked, lighting a cigarette.

'Oh, no. That's long over with. I just came to talk.'

'Good.' Crystal looked as if she wouldn't have cared much either way. 'Is he still with that firm of architects?'

'Yes. He's doing very well now.'

'Is that so?' Crystal exhaled a plume of smoke, her eyes speculative, regretful. 'Just goes to show.'

'He still talks about you,' Gala said. 'I think he's secretly still half in love with you.'

'No!'

'Oh yes. Jack's the most loyal person I know. *And* the most forgiving.'

A gleam of excitement lit Crystal's china-blue eyes. 'You serious? Fancy! I'd have thought he'd have forgotten me years ago.'

'Apparently not.' Suddenly uneasy, Gala rather regretted having told Crystal that. Jack was just susceptible enough to fall for any old line that this girl might care to shoot. *Do you really think Jack ought to have married Crystal?* Con's words echoed through her head, reminding her of the reason she'd come. 'So you didn't team up with Conrad Brandon in the end?' she asked, trying to inject a lighthearted note into the question. Crystal's face only soured.

'Doesn't look like it, does it?'

'The last time I saw you, you were going off to Barbados with him.' Gala sipped her coffee, trying to avoid the lipstick stain on the rim. 'Didn't it work out?'

'Not the way I planned it,' Crystal grunted. 'I ended up stuck in bloody Jamaica with no money and nowhere to stay. Luckily I bumped into this feller who was going to the States . . .'

'You mean Con just abandoned you there?' Gala asked, shocked.

'"Con"? You friendly with him?'

'Not exactly,' Gala said uncertainly. 'I've met him once or twice.'

'Yeah. Well, he did just leave me there.'

'I can't believe it! He took you all the way to Barbados, and then just dumped you?'

'Well. He didn't actually *take* me.'

'What?'

'I didn't actually go *with* him, if that's what you mean. I had plans, see. I was mad about him, and I reckon he was pretty keen on me, too. Until he found out about Jack. After that he kept giving me the brush-off. So when he went to Jamaica, I bought a ticket on the same flight.'

Disbelief made Gala blink. 'But—but—you were just about to get married to Jack!'

Crystal shrugged. 'I call them the Last Minute Blues. Same as I'm having now, with Len. I always get them.' She puffed at her cigarette. 'Some feller's always proposing to me, but every time it gets near the wedding-day, I get cold feet.' She grinned. 'Itchy feet, actually. I feel this terrible urge coming over me to take off over the horizon. I think it's psychological,' she said confidentially, not noticing Gala's frozen expression. 'Well, if you know Con Brandon you'll know what a dish he is. He was at a party that I went to one night, without Jack. He danced with me all night.' A dreamy look unfocused her eyes. 'The minute I met him, I thought I'd found my ideal man. And I got terrible Last Minute Blues about your Jack. So that's what happened.'

'I don't understand,' Gala stammered. 'You mean Con didn't seduce you?'

'I wish he had,' Crystal said feelingly. 'God, if I'd got my hooks into him I'd be well away now. Have you seen those hotels of his? And that car showroom? Yeah, Mrs Con Brandon would have suited me down to the ground. But he wasn't having any of it.'

'You never—never slept with him?'

'It wasn't for want of trying. And I can be *very* persuasive when I want to be.' Crystal exhaled a plume of smoke again. 'I chased him like mad in London. And then, when I found out he was going on holiday, I thought I had my chance.' She made a spitting sound. 'The whole thing was a bloody waste of time and money. And I'd bought all this sexy gear—bikinis and shorts and all the rest. Still, that came in useful in the States.'

'Crystal,' Gala said, dry-mouthed, 'are you telling me that there was really never anything between you and Con Brandon?'

'Not so much as a French kiss,' Crystal sighed. She stubbed her cigarette out. 'He didn't half give me hell when he found out I'd followed him to Barbados, too. Told me I was the biggest fool he'd ever met, which I couldn't exactly argue with.' She sighed. 'He went straight to the airline office and bought me a ticket home. But as I say, I met this Yank, and I managed to trade it for a ticket to New York. Then, when I arrived there, I went to this model agency——' Crystal was settling comfortably into the swing of her life-story, but Gala interrupted her, white-faced.

'But you told us you were having an affair with Con! You said he was taking you away with him!'

Crystal looked surprised. 'What odds does it make?'

'It makes odds to *me*,' Gala said fiercely.

'Keep your hair on. I just thought it would be easier on Jack than if he thought I was just bored with him. I didn't see that it made all that much difference—I mean, none of you even knew Con, so it was no skin off your noses. Besides, if things had turned out the way I wanted, it *would* have been true, wouldn't it?'

'And Con?' Gala said furiously. 'I suppose his reputation meant nothing to you?'

'Ach.' She dismissed that with a wave. 'That kind of thing doesn't harm a man's reputation. Makes him look more of a lad, if anything. All men want to be thought of as Casanovas . . .'

Gala sat stunned. Everything she'd ever thought about Con Brandon, everything she'd blindly taken for granted, was now crumbling around her. Crystal, not Con. It had been Crystal who'd betrayed Jack. Con's only fault had been that he was the focus of this selfish, stupid woman's desires.

And out of some misconceived loyalty to Jack and her family, she herself had insulted the man, rejected him, given him every cause in the world to hate her!

'So you say Jack's still interested in me?' Crystal

said, lighting another cigarette. She studied her nails casually. 'You know something, I wouldn't mind seeing him again. Just for old time's sake.'

'If you come near my brother,' Gala said savagely, 'I'll scratch your eyes out!' She stood up, her whole body rigid with unreasoning anger. 'He's just stupid enough to fall for you all over again—but I'm not. D'you hear me? Don't you come near him, not *ever*.'

Unmoved by Crystal's astounded expression, Gala ran to the door, a claustrophic frustration building up in her. How long had passed since she'd last seen Con? Two weeks? Dear God, she had to get to him immediately, try and beg his forgiveness——

'Hey!' Crystal Warren, looking frightened, came padding after her in her bare feet. 'Look, if I said anything wrong, I'm sorry!'

Gala didn't risk an answer. Her volcanic spurt of anger was giving way to anxiety already now. Crystal Warren's casual lie, told in a suburban living-room three years ago, might have already destroyed her only chance of happiness. What if he wouldn't listen to her? What if he'd already found someone else? What if . . .?

'Gala!' Crystal peered over the balcony as Gala ran to her car. 'Give my love to Jack!'

CHAPTER NINE

THE wind blew cold and rainy off the moors. Gala huddled into her mac for the minimal warmth it provided, her hair whipped in wet coppery strands across her face.

It was bitter cold. Still, there was a yellow sea of daffodils in the dank meadow, their resilient stems dancing in the wind, and when the wind clawed a hole in the clouds, a blue sky appeared for a few seconds at a time.

She hadn't been prepared for the crowds. There seemed to be thousands of people in this picturesque Yorkshire village, braving the spring cold in anoraks and scarves. The several hot-dog stands were doing brisk business with the spectators; but Gala noticed that the professionals, like the television crews and the rally officials, kept well in the shelter of caravans or the white outside broadcast pantechnicons, consulting the contents of lunch-tins and battered Thermos flasks.

The banner across the muddy dirt road billowed into a hoop, its scarlet letters proclaiming, 'Moors Rally: Fifth Stage'. But it was only four-thirty, and the cars weren't due until dinner-time. They'd only be stopping for a matter of hours. To cram down food and snatch sleep. The final stage of the rally would begin later on, an all-night unlimited-speed race through Forestry Commission land. She'd learned all this from the various people she'd spoken to earlier. She'd also learned that under the complicated scoring system, Con was currently in the lead.

Gala queued for a plastic cup of coffee, regretting

having left her own Thermos in London, and
retreated to her car, parked with the hundreds of
others in the village square.

'*Con isn't in London, I'm afraid.*' That was on
Monday. Disappointment had been sharp as a knife.
She'd rushed straight from Crystal's flat to the
Serafina, her mind churning with the things she
wanted to tell Con, and the news that he was gone had
seemed a black omen. It had made her heart sink.
Coral Bonnington had looked at Gala's pale face
curiously. 'He's racing in a big rally up North. Didn't
you know? The Moors Rally.'

'When will he be back?'

'Con isn't that predictable,' Coral smiled. 'He's got
some urgent business in New York, and he was talking
about taking Concorde after the race . . .'

'America?' Gala wailed.

'If it's urgent, why not go up and try to catch him
between stages? They stop every now and then, you
know. You might even enjoy it—I always do.'

It had taken her a whole maddening day to get her
schedules at work sorted out to give her the time off,
but Roger Trefusis had been marvellous. She'd set off
from London yesterday, travelling on the Great North
Road as fast as she dared, the aged Ital straining every
sprocket to get her there. She'd been lucky enough to
find a bed-and-breakfast cottage with a vacancy (oil-
lighting and five cows in the garden), but she'd hardly
slept in the lacy bedroom last night. Depression and
hope had been struggling inside her ever since. Con
was a fiercely proud man, and the look in his eyes the
last time they'd met had been almost one of hate. And
yet, that day in the woods—hadn't he more or less said
he loved her? Yes, but she'd thrown it back in his face.
What was she going to face? A cold rejection? Damn
Jack, damn his gullible, credulous nature.

No. She herself was the fool, the biggest fool of the

lot. She sipped the tasteless coffee, nerves jangling in her stomach. If she didn't win this stage of her own life, there would be no second chance. She knew that. The afternoon sun fizzled out under lowering clouds, and another long gust of rain swept the ancient grey stones of the village, rattling across the roof of her car and making her shiver. Behind the houses, the dim contours of the moors were almost lost in the mist. She switched on the car radio, hoping for distraction.

'. . . team is scoring high on averages. Brandon, twice British champion, is still in the lead despite several mishaps, but his position is threatened by at least three other drivers. It's in the special stages, however, that Conrad Brandon has always excelled, and in the final, gruelling dash across the daunting Black Rock Moor tomorrow, he and his team-mate Sandy Dickerson may well widen that narrow gap to give the Porsche team the victory they deserve.'

Gala wrapped her rug around her cold knees and sat listening to the light music that followed the news. She hadn't prepared any speeches for him. She couldn't ask him to forgive the crazy way she'd behaved. She could only beg him to give them a new beginning. Would he listen?

A few minutes before five-thirty, the first of the competitor's cars exploded out of the mist, almost unrecognisable in its coating of mud. The lashing rain didn't dampen the excitement of the crowds, some of whom had spent the whole afternoon waiting, and Gala was jostled mercilessly by people surging up to the barrier. With the cars came an escort of officials and cameramen in Land-Rovers and on motorbikes, and the public-address system added to the general level of noise by crackling out a commentary on the drivers.

Con's car, third across the line, was greeted with a ragged cheer. The low, muscular-looking machine was

plastered with mud and sponsor's decals in equal
proportions, its white paintwork barely visible. The
windows, apart from the track made by the back and
front wipers, were impenetrable, and all she could see
were two helmeted figures strapped into the bucket
seats. Her heart pounding, Gala watched the cars pass
through the controls, each co-driver reaching out a
card to be marked. In the general chaos she lost sight
of Con's car for a while. Her hair was soaked by the
time she'd pushed her way through the milling crowds
to where it had stopped.

Then she saw him, hauling off his helmet. The
white nylon suit he wore, like a pilot's, covered his
entire body, but his height set him apart from the rest
of the crowd. A group of people from the support
team were on hand to greet him. A lot of shouting and
back-slapping went on for a while, but Gala's heart
contracted at the weariness in the harsh, tanned face.
And the back-slapping gave way to concern as the co-
driver was helped out of his seat, looking limp. As
they supported him, he clutched his stomach.

'Con,' Gala called. The camera crews, scenting a
story, were hustling towards the two white-clad
figures, and someone pushed her aside roughly. She
regained her balance in time to catch someone saying,
'. . . probably his appendix—get the doctor as soon as
possible.'

'Con,' she shouted, trying to make herself heard
above the loudspeaker's boom which had started again
just then. She pushed herself through, grasping at his
sleeve. 'Con! I've got to talk to you.'

He glanced at her almost as though he didn't
recognise her. 'What the hell are you doing here?'

'I've come to apologise,' she blurted out. 'I saw
Crystal Warren on Monday, and she told me—oh,
Con, I'm so sorry——'

'There's no time right now,' he said curtly, cutting

through her stammering. He turned to answer a question one of the officials was asking him.

'*Con!*' Her voice made him swing round to her again. 'It's important!'

His eyes raked her face. 'Come to my caravan in an hour. Better make that an hour and a half. Got that?'

'Yes,' she nodded, feeling weak. 'Where is it?'

But he was already gone, being escorted away on a tide of people. A little giddy, Gala let herself be jostled in the opposite direction. Disappointment had her by the throat again. It was getting dark already. The rain was still pouring down, and still the cars were coming in, their headlights slashing through the mist, their engines snarling. She stopped an official hurrying past under a large multicoloured umbrella.

'Excuse me, do you know where Con—Conrad Brandon's caravan is?'

'It'll be with the Porsche team.' He pointed vaguely across the sodden field. 'Ask someone there. Excuse me, please.'

Alone in the rain, Gala suddenly wondered what on earth she was doing here. The unreality of it all hit her. What was she chasing Con for? He didn't want to see her, didn't want to know. The thread of self-confidence that had kept her going for the past couple of days seemed at last to have worn out and snapped. More miserable than ever, she crawled back into her car, and muffled herself in her rug. The Ice Princess was finally gone, melted away. At last Gala Fletcher had become a woman, warm, emotional, with feelings that surged in her heart. But was it all too late?

She'd learned the vital lesson—that her refusal to trust Con was more a reflection on her own personality than on his. That there had been something in her nature, a vulnerability, perhaps, left over from Brian, that had made her pathologically unable to trust anyone.

And that problem within herself, more than the accusation that Con had broken up Jack's engagement, more even than his playboy image, had come between them. It wasn't stupidity, there wasn't any question of blame. Just one of those strange veils that sometimes obscure even the best of intentions.

So—*she'd* managed to sort that out. Would Con? Would he ever have the patience to forgive her, let them have another chance?

At least he'd agreed to see her. At least she'd have the consolation of having *tried*.

It was very dark by seven. Flaring lamps lit the temporary workshop where half-a-dozen mechanics were working on the now spotless car Con had been driving, and as Gala walked across the wet grass she got the impression of a well-oiled team working in perfect unison.

Getting through the protective cordon of team members didn't prove easy, though. Two burly men in Pirelli T-shirts informed her acidly that Con was trying to get a few minutes' sleep, and could do without 'groupies'.

'I'm not a groupie,' she said, suddenly inspired. 'I'm Con's physiotherapist.' She scrabbled in her bag and pulled out her Parker Clinic identity card. 'He's under my treatment—he'll see me, I promise. Please!'

The bearded man inspected it dubiously. 'Ingenious, if nothing else.'

'He needs me! Hasn't he been complaining about his back?'

'Yeah, but he never said anything about . . .'

The clean-shaven man took the card and held it under his torch. 'Hey, Steve—this is Gala Fletcher. Aren't you the one who saved his life when he was practically crippled a couple of weeks ago?'

'Well, yes, but he wasn't exactly crippled . . .'

'Why didn't you say so before?' the bearded man

beamed. 'He wouldn't be here tonight if it wasn't for you—he's been raving about you, right, Al? Come on, we can't have *both* drivers sick.' He grabbed her arm and led her to a caravan pulled up away from the noise and light. 'He's in there, Miss Fletcher. Could you be as quick as you could? The whole thing starts again at nine.'

'Okay,' she nodded breathlessly, and tapped timidly at the door. There was no reply, and she let herself quietly in through the door.

The interior of the caravan was softly lit. As Gala's eyes adjusted, she saw that Con was sprawled on the bunk, hands clasped behind his neck. Her heart sank at the sight of his face. It was grim and set, the passionate mouth compressed to a hard line, the grey eyes cold as winter.

'I'm due to set off soon,' he said by way of greeting.

'I know,' Gala whispered.

'So. To what do I owe this visit?'

She'd never expected him to be quite so icy, so forbidding. 'Con,' she faltered, 'I met Crystal Warren on Monday. Completely by accident. She told me— she told me the way it was between you, that it wasn't your fault. I don't know—don't know what to say. I'm so sorry, so very sorry I behaved the way I did.'

'Sure.'

The monosyllable wasn't encouraging, but Gala struggled on. 'There's something else I want to say . . .'

'Hasn't everything been said?' he interrupted impatiently. 'You're sorry. Okay. Now let's forget the whole thing.'

'Is that what you really want?' Gala asked quietly. 'Once before you said you . . .'

'I what?' he demanded as she stopped. She lowered her eyes.

'You said you loved me.'

'Did I?' Hard mockery made his voice derisive.

'I think you did.' She stood in silence as he filled his cup with black coffee from the jug beside him and gulped it down. 'Con, don't let it end like this, please. We had so much going for us . . .'

'You certainly pick your times.'

The interruption cut her short. 'What?'

'You do realise that this is the first chance I've had to rest in twelve hours of non-stop driving? That my navigator is currently doubled up with suspected appendicitis in the medical tent? That I have to set off for the all-night stage within two hours?' Gala found it in herself to smile wryly. It hadn't even occurred to her, in her misery, that this might not be the most appropriate stage to unload all her personal guilt and emotion on to Con. Nothing else had seemed to matter until now.

'Oh, Con, I know it's a terrible time and place, but I couldn't have borne not seeing you again. Don't be angry with me. I didn't even know whether you'd be coming back to London. Coral said you might be going to America . . .'

'I am.' He sat upright, unzipping the nylon tunic and peeling it away from his naked shoulders. 'While you're here you might as well be of use,' he said brutally. 'My back's playing up again. Can you do anything?'

'Oh, no.' The news jerked her into her professional gear immediately, giving her a kind of instant strength. She pulled off her own wet mac and went to him. 'You're crazy, you know that?' she accused shakily. 'Damn you, why did you have to race so soon after your injury? You've probably strained those muscles all over again!' God, how much she cared for him! If only he knew how much he mattered to her . . . Trying to thrust her turbulent and yearning feelings of love to the back of her mind, she made him lie flat on his stomach, and probed his muscular back with expert fingers. 'What happened?'

'We hit a bad pothole at Rosebury,' he said into the pillow. 'I thought I felt something go. That's also where Sally's stomach started playing up badly.'

She could feel the muscles, locked like steel plates. Just like before. He'd started racing far too soon after his recovery. Damn! 'Have you got any oil?'

'The mechanics bring gallons of the stuff,' he said drily. 'Multigrade or super?'

'This is no time for jokes.' She ran through to the tiny bathroom. In the cabinet she found what she wanted, a tube of hand-cream that would do. Smearing the oil across his skin, she hiked up her skirts unceremoniously, straddled his hips, and started massaging his back carefully.

Con sighed, closing his eyes. 'Aah, that's good.'

'You've got to give up rallying,' she said through clenched teeth, her palms pressing into his hard flesh.

'And you've got to give up nagging me,' he retorted calmly. 'Do physiotherapists always sit on their patient's bottoms?'

'I'm so ashamed of myself, Con.' She wiped her auburn hair out of her eyes, oblivious to the oil she was getting on it. She needed to make him understand, if it was the last thing she did. 'Please listen to me—there's so much I want to say. From the very first I've tried to hate you because of Crystal. It seems so crazy now, so crazy of me to make so much of that one shadow . . .'

'It wasn't just Crystal,' he said quietly. 'Crystal was only a peg for you to hang other things on.'

Gala paused, her hands resting on his gleaming skin. 'Like what?'

'Like the offer of a relationship you couldn't handle. Because you couldn't handle it, could you? It was all too much for you. Every time you were asked to feel an emotion or give a little love, you had to retreat into your starched white shell.'

'That's all in the past now,' she said in a low voice. 'I've changed, Con. You've changed me.'

'Have I?' Sceptical lines curved round his mouth. 'I wasn't entirely kidding you about the whiptail lizards, Gala. You've got yourself into a way of life that just doesn't have any place for desire. Or love. And you've always hated me for bringing those things into it.' He shifted his shoulders. 'Don't stop, that was just beginning to ease the pain.'

His words had slammed home, body-blows that shook her. 'You know me better than I know myself,' she said quietly, starting again. 'You always have. I *was* cold, I *was* pompous. A fool, yes. Everything you accuse me of. But though I was ridiculously mistaken about you and Crystal, you *must* believe me when I say that it cast a huge shadow over me. Okay, it was ridiculously childish of me to believe it, not to check out the facts—but I let it worry me half to death. I had Jack coming round, threatening all sorts of family sanctions if I didn't stop seeing you.' She drew an unsteady breath. His eyes were closed, but whether or not he was listening to her monologue she couldn't tell. 'I'm not very experienced, Con. I—I've only had one lover. Apart from you, that is. And he wasn't— well, he wasn't very nice. Maybe neither of us were.' She shook her head. Someday she was going to have to tell him about Brian—but not now. 'Maybe I got the idea somehow that it was better not to feel—or not to acknowledge feelings. But I feel I've grown up by about ten years in these past weeks.' She paused again. 'Is your back any better?'

'Much.' He stretched luxuriously, muscles rippling. 'You're a rotten lover, but you're a hell of a masseuse.'

She didn't reply to the taunt. 'I can feel the spasm

easing. When this race is finished, will you promise to let me give you some more treatment?'

'Maybe,' he said indifferently, eyes shut.

'You'll need it.' She paused. 'Are you going to forgive me, Con?'

'I'm not the forgiving type.' With unexpected power, he rolled her over, laying her flat on her back and leaning across her, his mouth threateningly close to her own. 'And I don't know if you're worth it, Ms Fletcher.'

'Why didn't you just put me over your knee?' Drowning in his eyes, adoring him, she touched his cheek softly. 'Last time, when I was lecturing you like a Sunday-School teacher. God, it makes me blush to think of it. Why didn't you just tip me over your knee and wallop me?'

Con's eyes narrowed. 'Don't think I wasn't tempted. It wouldn't have done any good, though.'

'But that was what I wanted, deep down!'

He stared at her mouth with hooded eyes. 'Was it? Perhaps I knew. But I also knew it would mean more—and hurt more—when you found out for yourself.'

'That's sadism,' she accused.

'*C'est brutal—mais ca marche.*' The wolf-howl of an engine being tested in the night outside broke into the intimacy of their world.

'I *am* worth it,' she said urgently. 'I swear I am. You've only seen the worst of me, Con. I could make you so happy—if you'd let me.' She struggled for the words to express her meaning, faced with his harsh, unsmiling gaze. 'At least give us a second chance together!'

'Perhaps you should prove something first,' he said slowly, lashes veiling his expression.

'Like what?'

'Prove that we make a good pair. Come with me on the final stage tonight.'

'You're joking.' She smiled, her hands caressing his skin. 'Aren't you?'

'I'm not. You told me you could read a map, didn't you?'

'I can! But *Con*.' She looked up at him in protest. The fjord-deep eyes were bright, but they definitely weren't teasing. 'You mean—come with you? In the car?' she asked in dawning horror.

'I mean you're going to replace my sick navigator. It won't be that difficult, so don't look so appalled.' He took her chin in a hard grip, and stared at her face as though he could read her soul there. 'You think we'd be good together? Then show me.'

'But I'd be lost . . .' she groaned, horrified at the proposal.

'You wouldn't be lost. This final stage is a flyer. From the navigating viewpoint it's straightforward enough—it'll be a doddle for you. All the complicated stuff is long over, anyway, and everything depends on speed now. Sally's got suspected appendicitis, and someone will have to replace him. It might as well be you as any other idiot. All the navigator has to do is sit tight and give directions—which you're very good at,' he added silkily. 'Besides, you have the advantage of being lighter than any man. All you'll need to do is keep us on the right track.'

'But—but you're in the lead, Con!' The whole idea was so crazy that she found herself stammering. 'I'll ruin everything for you!'

'You'd better not,' he said grimly. 'And the sponsors will love the publicity. Think of the finish, when you pull your helmet off and let loose all that golden-red hair.'

'No!' Protesting against the idea, Gala sat up. 'Don't make me!'

'Call it your penance for thinking the worst of me all these weeks,' he said drily. 'Yes or no?'

'You're really serious,' she said, nerves beginning to jump in her stomach.

'It's an interesting idea,' he shrugged. But he was watching her intently. 'I don't promise anything afterwards, Gala. Just that I'll reconsider.'

'If it means earning a new start for you and me, Con,' she said quietly, 'you know I'd do anything.'

'Right.' The assessing look was gone. 'Time's running short.' He got up, pulling her easily to her feet. 'We've got to get moving immediately. There's a lot to do.'

She was still reeling. She'd come here to talk to him, to pour out her heart, and had been caught up in a whirlwind. 'But what about my car? What about——'

'Never mind all that,' he said brusquely, hauling on his nylon suit. 'That will all come later.' He grinned savagely. 'You're going to have to start learning to obey for once in your young life, understand?'

'I promise I will,' she said fervently.

'We'll see,' he said sarcastically. His eyes were suddenly icy again. 'Don't get what I say next wrong, Gala. It doesn't mean anything. But if I'm to sell this idea to the team, I need you to join me in a minor deception. I need to tell them we're engaged.'

'Engaged?' she said numbly.

'It means nothing, like I said.' His voice was harsh. 'They wouldn't countenance the idea of you joining me otherwise. Do you agree?'

Pain twisted in her. With deadly accuracy, he knew how to hit the most painful targets in her heart. The killer instinct. Yet she'd deserved this kind of cruelty. 'Did I hurt you like this?' she asked in a low voice. 'If I did, I'm sorry.'

'Don't be a sentimental idiot,' he said acidly. 'Do you agree to the deception or not?'

'I agree,' she said, her face pale.

'And you agree that it means nothing?'

She dropped her eyes, feeling the pain come again. 'Yes.' The word was almost a whisper.

'Then let's go.' He turned to go, obviously quite unmoved by the way she'd been affected. She caught her breath and followed him out of the door, wondering whether this was all a weird dream that would suddenly disappear around her like smoke, leaving nothing of its pain, anxiety and confusion.

In the neon-lit interior of the team caravan, a group of twelve or fifteen team-members were working excitedly on preparations for the last stage. Con took her arm with strong fingers. 'Play up. Right?' Then he ushered her inside, receiving a rapturous welcome.

'Ready to go?' Steve, the bearded Pirelli man asked, slapping him on the shoulder. For the first time, Gala noticed that he wore a cap reading *Chief Technician*. 'Did your physiotherapist fix you up again?'

'She did.' He rapped calmly on a table for silence. 'Can I have your attention, everyone. I'd like you all to meet Miss Gala Fletcher.'

'Ah.' An attractive, authoritative-looking woman of about thirty-five, with *Team Manager* embroidered on her jacket came to shake Gala's hand. 'My name's Zelda Winship. Steve told us you were here. Thanks for coming. You've worked wonders with our champion, Miss Fletcher. I had to practically break his arm to get him to ask for treatment in the first place.'

Gala nodded nervous thanks, her throat dry.

'Gala and I have just become engaged,' Con said, his eyes resting on Gala's with a slight smile. He slid his arm round her waist, making her ache. 'We're getting married.'

There was a dead silence. Gala stared helplessly at the frozen tableau of officials and support workers, all of whom seemed to have stopped in mid-task to stare at her. But for Con's arm around her, she was sure she would have slid to the ground.

'Married?' Steve repeated, looking slightly stunned. Grins began to appear all round.

'*Married?*' Zelda blinked. 'Are you serious?'

'Never more so,' Con nodded, eyes glinting. 'Some time next month, if all goes well. I trust you're all going to make it.'

'You're damn right we're going to make it,' a mechanic said, his smile breaking gleaming white in his oily face. 'Why, you old son-of-a-gun!' There was a whoop of celebratory delight, and suddenly people she'd never seen in her life before were kissing her cheek and slapping her back. It was so hard to smile back when the bitter irony was eating at her from within. God, if only this was real, and not an empty charade! Only the thought that this might mean a new chance for her gave her the strength to go on.

'There's something else,' Con said, shouting to make himself heard. 'Gala's coming with me on the last stage.' There was another stunned silence. His eyes met the team manager's. 'She's an expert navigator. And if I get pains again, she'll know what to do. Just think of the fabulous publicity, Zelda,' he went on smoothly. 'The winning car screams up to the line, and out gets the champion—and lo and behold, a gorgeous red-head beside him. Who is she, everyone wants to know?' He grinned. 'I can see the headlines now—champion wins race with future bride in navigator's seat. It's never been done before.'

'This isn't my idea,' Gala said in a small voice.

'I never imagined it was,' Zelda said with a smile. Her eyes grew serious. 'Think you can do it?'

'If Con thinks so,' she stammered. 'I've never done anything like this before . . .'

'She can do anything,' Con said calmly. 'She's also light, quick, and sharp-sighted.'

'You realise it's very dangerous?' Steve asked, looking at Gala's pale face.

'Can you read a map?' someone else asked.

'My father taught me,' she nodded. 'He was an airline pilot.'

'Marvellous,' Steve said, beaming. 'If you don't mind being flung about a little?'

'I'll do anything,' she said, glancing at Con's smiling face. And that was the truest thing in this whole mad game, she thought wryly.

'The final stage isn't very tricky anyway,' Zelda put in. Her expression was intent. 'You know, this might just be a splendid idea, Con.'

'Of course it's a splendid idea,' he grinned. 'Think the officials will swallow it?'

'If she pays her entrance fee, I don't see why not.' Zelda looked at Gala quizzically. 'You don't look altogether happy about this, Gala!'

'Oh, I am,' she said, trying to brighten her expression. 'I just hope to God we don't end up in Manchester.'

Suddenly everyone was laughing.

CHAPTER TEN

THE cockpit was as stark and grim as a jet-fighter's, reinforced with naked steel roll-bars. Everything was matt-black, making the glow of the instruments seem all the brighter. The note of the engine was a fearsome howl that made conversation almost impossible at times.

'I thought there'd at least be a *road*,' Gala yelled at Con. 'This is just a track!' He nodded, absorbed in the task of keeping the wildly bucking car from rocketing off the steep slopes to either side. In the pitch darkness, the blaze of the car's six huge lamps showed a rugged landscape of moor and rock, blurred with speed. Occasionally the bright beams would stab into nothingness as they hurtled over a crest, as they did now.

'Ouch!' Gala's helmeted head banged against the roll-bar with a dull thud. He spared her a lightning grin.

'Enjoying yourself?'

'It's terrifying!' But the strange thing was that she *was* enjoying it—in a fraught way. Her spirits had lifted sky-high. 'You're the best driver I've ever known,' she volunteered, 'but you still scare me stiff!' They'd been driving for almost an hour now, and they had already left the closest car more than a mile behind. This was an utterly different experience from the last time she and Con had driven together. For the first time she was realising what a savagely demanding sport this was, calling for the utmost control and co-ordination. But for the webbing harness which strapped them both into their seats, they would already be bruised solid.

She yelped again as the car jarred viciously over loose stones. 'And I'm not even insured.'

'Stop complaining,' he said unsympathetically, 'and start navigating.'

Obediently, she pulled the illuminated map-magnifier off the dashboard to study the map spread out on her thighs. She was wearing a spare suit that had been found for her at the last minute; it was a size or two too big, but it was at least warm.

'Con,' she called, 'there's a sharp right turn somewhere along this road.' They flew over a crest, the car seeming to revel in the wild motion. 'There it is!' But they'd overshot the turning. There was no three-point turn. Con jerked up the handbrake and swung the wheel, and the car slewed neatly in its own length to face in the opposite direction. 'Help,' Gala said weakly. She'd only seen stuff like this in films. With a snarl of skidding tyres they set off again, and Con slammed the car round the corner on to a steep hillside road. She had time to notice that the speedometer was reading an unbelievable 90 as they snaked down the twisty, loose-surfaced track.

'Where are we?' he asked, hands and feet moving with hypnotic precision on the controls.

'Just about to cross the Moor itself.' She tried to hold the map still. 'In about ten miles we'll pass a passage control.' That, they carefully explained to her, was a control point on the route, set up to check that the competitors were following the prescribed route. Con simply nodded. A gust of rain slashed across the windscreen. He was driving with a ruthless skill that almost frightened her, accelerating so hard at times that she was crushed against the bucket seat, revving the powerful engine until the scream was sometimes more than her ears could bear.

'I never knew about Jack,' he said suddenly. 'Not that I was ever serious about Crystal anyway—but she

never told me she was engaged to Jack. Not until
much later. And then I refused to have anything more
to do with her.'

'I know.' Gala looked across at him. The helmet
made him look fiercely male, like some warrior chief.
'Crystal told me the whole story. Did you sleep with
her?'

'No.' He accelerated hard through a small ford,
water spraying out into the night on either side, and
glanced at her again. 'But would it have hurt you if I'd
said I had?'

'I didn't know you cared about hurting me,' she
offered with wry amusement. 'But no, it wouldn't
hurt. Not now. Nobody else really matters any more—
except you.'

'Very touching,' he grunted. 'When she turned up
in Barbados, telling everyone that I'd brought her
with me, I was furious. I bought her a ticket back to
Heathrow, but the next I heard, she was in the States.'

'She's engaged to a patient of mine now.' Gala
sighed, thinking back on all the misery that Crystal
Warren had caused with her thoughtless lies. 'The
poor man. He thinks she's wonderful. I don't think
he's got the remotest idea what she's really like.'

'Oh,' Con said, 'I wouldn't worry about Len Bullen.
He can take care of himself.'

'You know him?' Gala asked, surprised.

'I sold him his last three Jaguars.' His smile was
wicked. 'I also recommended him to go to you about
his arm.'

'You did?' Recollection made her blink. 'But Len
said someone called Bertie something or other had
recommended him . . .'

'Bertie Naylor. Just a little joke between Len and
me.'

'You   mean   *you*   planned   the   whole . . .?'
Bewilderment was shot through with the realisation

that he wasn't as indifferent to her as he'd pretended. 'Why, you Macchiavellian devil!'

'You didn't think I was going to just sit around while you bumbled around after the truth?' They were slaloming down through a rough cutting, the powerful engine growling in protest as Con used the iron-clawed discipline of the huge disc brakes. She could hardly think straight in the welter of impulses homing in on her brain.

'You're utterly amazing,' she gasped, not knowing whether to be delighted, appalled or amused at his machinations. 'I don't think I'd ever try and cross you, Con—I wouldn't dare! Have you dreamed this whole scheme up on my behalf?'

'It all worked out rather neatly,' Con smiled. 'And I'm not as Macchiavellian as you think. It was pure coincidence that I found out Len was getting married to Crystal. I had no qualms about sending him to you about his arm—you're brilliant.' He swung the wheel swiftly to avoid a series of pot-holes, and glanced at her with bright eyes. 'I just asked him to mention that Crystal was back in London. I knew that would get you. But I didn't think you'd go and see her so soon. And I certainly didn't expect you to arrive in the middle of a rally, dripping remorse and self-knowledge.'

'What? With my whole happiness in the balance?' Gala shook her head. 'You've always made me seem so predictable, Con. You must have known I couldn't have stopped myself from going to see her!' The suspicion that it might be going to be all right, after all, rose in her heart like a sunrise. 'Would you have come for me if I hadn't gone to see Crystal?' she asked in a small voice. 'Or would you just have put me out of your mind for ever and found someone else?'

'You're so beautiful,' he said obliquely. 'I always found your colours ravishing, right from the first.

Lucky I didn't know what a spitfire you were under that lovely exterior, though.'

'Don't make me wait like this,' she begged. 'Tell me I'm forgiven, *please*.'

His voice was feather-light, almost unheard against the roar of the engine. 'You were always forgiven, Gala.'

She stared at him a few seconds longer, then closed her eyes against the tears. 'Oh, darling,' she choked, 'I love you so much . . .'

'I know,' he said mildly, bringing the car to a tyre-screaming halt. 'Don't cry on the map. Give the man the card.' An official in a dripping coat had emerged from a Rally Supervisor's caravan to stamp their card with the time. Gala smeared the tears off her cheeks, trying not to dissolve into helpless female emotion. But her heart was bursting with happiness, as though a whole new person had been crammed into her, a person whose capacity for joy was suddenly as unlimited as the sky. Her stomach seemed to press against her backbone as Con accelerated away hard, whipping through the gearbox to reach almost eighty within seconds. 'You've loved me for weeks, silly girl,' he went on, eyes studying the mirror to check for rivals. 'But you didn't know it yourself. You've been fighting against it as though it were the worst thing in the world—instead of the best.' He hooked one arm around her shoulders, and for a brief second hugged her to him hard, their helmets clashing together. The rough caress was the sweetest thing she'd ever known. 'That's why I thought it best to let you stew a while. Yes, of course I would have come for you. But remember what I once told you? It's best to learn these things where and when they happen. That way the lesson lasts.'

'Con . . .' It was so good to be alive, to be speeding through the night towards a new life with the man she loved. Everything melted into the release of her love, the dark, rushing world outside blurring into oblivion.

'By the way,' Con went on, 'Len's not as blind to Crystal's faults as he seems. He knows all about her, but he's the sort of man who'll forgive anything. He might also be the only man able to keep Crystal Warren under control. A sort of father-figure.'

'I'm glad *you're* not a father-figure,' Gala sighed, and he laughed. This explosive finish wasn't allowing her time to think, time to absorb the dazzling happiness that was hers. Maybe it would always be like this with Con. Always something new, always excitement and change, always this fantastic together-ness that had welded them from the start. 'How could you be so cold to me back at the caravan?' she demanded.

'I didn't see why you should have it too easy,' he smiled.

'I've *never* had it easy,' she wailed. 'You've been really horrible to me at times!'

'You deserved it,' he said briskly. 'Besides, you said some perfectly foul things to me. Or have you forgotten? You once said I was the most dishonourable man you knew.'

'Did I?' Flushing hotly at her own folly, Gala looked out of the window to avoid his glance.

'You also ran off like a mad thing in the middle of a forest,' he went on blandly.

'Oh no.' Gala winced. 'Don't remind me of all the stupid things I've done. Did you really follow me that afternoon?'

'Of course,' he shrugged. 'Anything could have happened to you. The one useful thing I learned in the Army was how to move silently.' The track was climbing steeply now, the headlights giving fitful hints of a mass of dark trees up ahead. 'I had a lot of fun teasing you,' he admitted unashamedly. 'You rose to the bait with unfailing regularity. 'You're a lot wiser now.'

'Am I?' She reached out to touch his arm momentarily. 'I feel wiser. And so much happier than I was, Con.'

'You're a good kid,' he grinned.

'I'm not a kid—I'm a woman.'

'Yes.' He looked at her, eyes warm. 'Yes, you are. From the moment I saw you, I wanted you, Gala. You haunted me, with your cool green eyes, your beauty, your grace, your hidden passion! I knew I had to possess you or never find rest again.' He smiled quietly, tracing the smooth curve of her thigh with his fingers. 'I didn't count on it being such a struggle.'

'It'll never be a struggle again,' she promised unevenly. His touch was bliss, his words like water on parched soil, a promise of new life. 'I'm yours, Con, for what I'm worth. However you want me, whenever.'

'Large promises.' He brought the car to another ferocious halt, this time switching off the engine. In the silence her ears rang.

'What . . .?'

He pulled off his helmet, and let it tumble on to the floor, then reached for her. 'To hell with it, I've got to touch you.'

'But your race——'

'We're miles ahead.' Their mouths met, hungry for each other, giving and receiving with an intensity of passion that shook her to her soul. She fumbled briefly with the strap of her own helmet, then simply gave in to the devastation of submitting to his potent will. 'Sweet girl,' he said in a husky sigh, 'you make me want you so badly.' And she found that her hands were shaking as they explored the crisp curls of his hair.

'Con,' she sighed as his mouth touched her eyelids, 'don't ever leave me . . .'

'I never will,' he whispered. He kissed away the remaining tears from her lashes before taking her mouth in a declaration of desire and adoration that left her gasping for him.

'The race,' she whispered weakly. 'You've got to win! You can't stop like this . . .'

'No?' He laughed softly. 'If you say so. Yes, I do want to win this rally. And I'm glad you're here to share it with me, my love. It's my last.'

'Your *last*?' Flabbergasted, Gala stared at him. 'Are you serious?'

'If I'm to make the transition from reckless playboy to respectable husband, I might as well do it thoroughly.' Her heart contracted painfully at the words, and Con smiled at her expression. 'Yes, I'm serious. I've won enough races, Gala. You've made me want other things. A family. Love.' His fingers bit into her shoulders. 'The only reason I kept rallying for all those years was because my life didn't have those things. I had women, yes—but not love, never love. I never found the right person, the woman I could love and respect. So I needed the excitement and absorption of racing to fill a gap, to make up for what wasn't there. Now that I've got you beside me, I'll never need anything again.'

'My darling——'

He kissed the words off her mouth and reached for his helmet.

'Tell me later, when I've got time to let it all sink in.' The engine thundered into life again as he twisted the key. 'What's the time, love?'

Gala peered numbly at the chronometer they'd given her. 'Three a.m.,' she said. 'Can it really be?'

'Time flies when you're having fun.' The wheels fought for a grip under the savage acceleration, and then they were storming up the bends through the forest. 'We ought to be at the finish by dawn. And then the celebrations will begin in earnest. And we'll have a wedding to organise, for one thing.' He glanced at her, as if by afterthought. 'You are going to marry me, aren't you?'

'Oh, yes.' Gala nodded like a blissful marionette. 'If you say so, I am.'

'In which case,' he said contentedly, 'absolutely nothing stands in the way of our winning this little race, my darling.'

'We'll be back in London tomorrow, Mum. Yes— bless you too. Give my love to Dad. 'Bye.'

Gala put the receiver down and lay back on the hotel bed, exhaustion and complete happiness making her feel as though she were floating several feet above herself. Something rustled beside her. It was the laurel garland. She was still soaring, hours after their barnstorming victory at eight that morning. Breakfast had consisted mostly of champagne, but it wasn't the wine that had made her giddy. The whole world had seemed to be celebrating with them; news of the romantic last stage had spread like wildfire, and there had been an army of media people to greet them—and an even bigger army of delighted spectators. So many congratulations, so many photographs and interviews and press conferences. Thrilling, but also draining. Celebrity was something she'd be delighted to do without for the rest of her life!

She reached out and touched the silken ribbons threaded through the leaves that proclaimed *Moors Rally*—*1st Place*. She was still in the vast, fluffy robe she'd put on after her shower, her auburn hair tumbled and glinting around her face. A romantic, sexy figure. What a long, long way she'd come from the prim Ice Princess she'd been such a short time ago . . .

Con emerged from the shower, his towel wrapped round his waist. His naked torso reminded her sharply, sweetly, of the first time she'd seen him, so arrogantly male at the poolside.

'You're smiling like the cat that's got the cream,' he commented, coming to sit beside her. He smelled of expensive aftershave, and she sniffed appreciatively.

'Maybe I'm just that.'

'So,' he asked, 'how did your parents react to the news that you're going to marry me?'

'Amazingly enough,' she sighed, rubbing her cheek against his hand, 'they're rather thrilled. Things are working out in the strangest way. Apparently Crystal went to see Jack, hoping to get herself in with him again. Can you believe that?'

'With Crystal,' Con grimaced, 'I can believe *anything*. So what happened?'

'She spilled the whole story about you and Bermuda and all the rest of it, admitting it was all false. I suppose she wanted to impress him with the fact that she hadn't had an affair with you. And suddenly Jack saw the light.' She shook her head, thinking of her brother's complicated, sensitive nature.

'And gave her the order of the boot?' Con enquired callously.

'Yes,' she nodded. 'Life's full of ironies, isn't it?'

'Hmm.' Con's eyes were narrowed thoughtfully. 'She'll go back to Len, now. That's good—I wouldn't want him hurt, and maybe they'll make their marriage work, after all. So everything's neatly settled.'

'Jack's a strange person,' she sighed. 'After three years of grieving and regret, he's finally seen what Crystal's really like. I've just spoken to him—he's quite jolly about the whole thing. Says he feels like a new man.'

'Bully for him,' Con said, kissing her petal-soft mouth.

'Don't be cross with Jack,' she pleaded, caressing his face. 'He was very, very apologetic about all the things he's said. And my parents are quite horror-stricken at having thought so badly of you. They're dying to meet you—but they're also rather terrified of you.' She smiled gently. 'You have that effect on people.'

'But not on you?' he asked in a velvety voice, quirking an eyebrow.

'Not any more, Con. Nothing scares me now—except the thought of losing you again.'

He smiled quietly, tracing the beautiful line of her cheekbone with one finger. 'I don't think there's much danger of that. I love you, you see.' Their lips touched with overwhelming gentleness, their hands interlacing in lover's patterns. 'I need you, Gala. For ever.'

'I love you,' she told him, the words taking on a meaning she'd never dreamed they could have.

'And I love you, sweet girl.'

'When does forever start?' she whispered, losing herself in the warm grey-blue of his eyes.

'Right now,' he said firmly. 'We're going to spend the remainder of the day in bed. You need plenty of rest if you're to be fit enough for a honeymoon in the South Seas next month.'

'You don't look as though you've got rest in mind,' she murmured, closing her eyes as he gently eased her robe aside.

'What I've got in mind,' he growled, 'would make you blush to the ends of your beautiful fingers.'

She half-opened languorous eyes as his lips began to find the sweetest, most sensitive places on her body.

'Really?'

'Really.'

'Then you'd better not tell me about it,' she smiled, arching against his body. 'Just do it . . .'

'Oh, I'm going to,' he purred. 'Again and again. And again.'

ROMANCE

Next month's romances from Mills & Boon

Each month, you can choose from a world of variety in romance with Mills & Boon. These are the new titles to look out for next month.

CAPRICORN MAN Jacqueline Gilbert
BUSHRANGER'S MOUNTAIN Victoria Gordon
BIG SUR Elizabeth Graham
THE OBJECT OF THE GAME Vanessa James
TAKEN OVER Penny Jordan
HOSTAGE Madeleine Ker
DARK OBSESSION Valerie Marsh
TRUST IN TOMORROW Carole Mortimer
MODEL OF DECEPTION Margaret Pargeter
DOUBLE DECEPTION Kay Thorpe

Buy them from your usual paperback stockist, or write to: Mills & Boon Reader Service, P.O. Box 236, Thornton Rd, Croydon, Surrey CR9 3RU, England. Readers in South Africa-write to: Mills & Boon Reader Service of Southern Africa, Private Bag X3010, Randburg, 2125.

Mills & Boon
the rose of romance

Mills & Boon

Take 4
Exciting Books
Absolutely
FREE

Love, romance, intrigue... all are captured for you by Mills & Boon's top-selling authors. By becoming a regular reader of Mills & Boon's Romances you can enjoy 6 superb new titles every month plus a whole range of special benefits: your very own personal membership card, a free monthly newsletter packed with recipes, competitions, exclusive book offers and a monthly guide to the stars, plus extra bargain offers and big cash savings.

**AND an Introductory FREE GIFT for YOU.
Turn over the page for details.**